Mrs. O'

Mrs. O'

****

by CLAUDE

Rinehart & Company, Inc.   New York

To George de Menasce

Preface

Se non è vero, è ben trovato

If this were an entirely accurate account of my life in Cork, I should probably be writing it behind bars. So I should say that it is impressionalistically true when not always factually so. I found Cork people and life in my Cork pub to be as I describe them, but for obvious reasons none of the characters are portraits of people, and none of the incidents are exact reporting. But it is not fiction, inasmuch as Ireland is an unreal place anyway, where the unlikely seems to happen more often than anything else, to me at least, and, if anything, this book is an overexposed photograph taken through the distorting lens of affection, delight and reminiscence.

CLAUDE

Contents

Mrs. O'

Having inherited a sizable legacy and considering herself a connoisseur of bars, the leading character in this book buys a pub in Cork. Here are a series of vignettes, as seen from the other side of the bar, of her customers.

1 ⁙ Over the Counter

I thought I knew all about pubs. From the outside of the counter, of course. A life-time of travelling had made me familiar with Biergartens, Tavernas, cafés, public-houses, the Ritz Bar and Dirty Dick's in Limehouse. I like drinking companionably, and I like to see others at it. I have been to an annual banquet of the London Bartenders, and have eaten apricot jam washed down with spring water with the landlord of a tiny Greek inn. I've drunk rye with Americans, schnapps with Dutchmen, beer with Germans, wine with Frenchmen, liqueurs with duchesses and gin with charladies. My father trained me early, before I was allowed to touch a drop, to mix a good Martini, saying this was as useful knowledge to a young woman as darning or knitting. "More useful," he added thoughtfully, "because most men don't know one darn from another unless it hurts; but one of those *mean* Martinis, half gin and half vermouth—they *always* hurt."

If there were a sign of the Zodiac called Bacchus, I'm sure I would have been born under it, but I never dreamed that I should eventually pass from my native Taurus into the domain of Hebe. It came about in the way of all predestined things—without premeditation.

At thirty I found myself for the first time alone and

independent. My decree absolute came through on the same day as my Great Aunt's legacy—not a fortune, but such a sum as I had never dreamed of owning or saving. I was in London at the time, my pleasure in the relaxation of war-time restrictions insufficient to compensate for the flat feeling I had of being just another troglodyte, unanchored in the intestines of the Underground. I left the chambers of Great Aunt's executors with mixed emotions, and walked slowly down the Strand ("wiv me gloves in me 'and") telling my-self, "Money. All that money. You're rich, my girl. How does it feel to be rich, eh?" And answered myself sadly and silently that it didn't feel like anything in particular. Mooney's Irish House was just opening its doors, and I went in, partly because I felt that I should be celebrating, and partly to steady myself. Money that doesn't come in a pay-packet always makes me shaky.

Mooney's is a fascinating blend of dissimilar places: a Wild West mirrored saloon (you almost expect young women in feather boas and black net stockings to lean over gamblers' shoulders), a railway refreshment room, a hotel pantry—what you will. The bar stretches a full eighty feet into the gloom—a gloom compounded of mahogany, panelled walls, and brass rails. Spittoons (yes, I'm sure there were spittoons) lined the walls, and the bartenders had rolled-up sleeves, waistcoats like provincial *garçons*, and long shin-length aprons. They looked, at eleven that morning, austere and priestly. There were some tables and chairs, but the vast bar had an attraction of its own and I did not sit down. There were already some customers drinking, and I observed them curiously. They were all Irish—every man-jack of them—and so were most of the bartenders, only the occasional Cock-ney twang breaking into the soft buzz of brogues. It was a novel experience to me and, fired with emulation, I ordered Irish whisky. "John Jameson's or Paddy?" I was asked.

The latter sounded too right to be ignored; I found it to be very like good rye, and the barman observed my appreciative gulp with approval. Leaning across the counter he said in confidential tones, "Sure, 'tis the best Irish whisky there is. It's scarce, though—even in Dublin you can't always get it. Comes from Cork. I'm from Kerry meself, but I must hand it to the Corkmen when it comes to whisky. 'Course, the English don't know the difference. . . . No offence. . . ."

Was it then that I suddenly realized that I could afford a holiday—a holiday in Ireland? I had never thought of going there before, and I wondered why. My childhood, under the aegis of Nanny, had been full of leprechauns and tinkers, harps and shamrocks, and St. Patrick's Day had ranked with the highest holidays. How could I have forgotten?

Two days later I was touching down at Shannon Airport, saying good-bye to the lovely Aer Lingus hostess from County Clare, who had somehow managed to make the conventional flight feel like a journey in Cinderella's coach. The unbelievable green of the land seen from a few hundred feet up had made me rub my eyes. She saw me and laughed. "No one believes this really is the Emerald Isle until they've flown in!"

Feeling gayer and more adventurous than I had in years, I resolved to have a really good look at the country, and with this object in mind I hired a small Standard from a Dublin firm. But even in the lands of the free, some formalities must be observed, and I had to obtain an Irish driving license. I was not made to take a test, having an international permit, but this was inspected with enormous care, as if it were in hieroglyphics. Finally, the representative of the Garda Siochana (the Police) who dealt with these matters, read out slowly and with obvious pleasure the names of the cities where the dog-eared document had been stamped: "Rome, Geneva, Madrid, Athens," and then sucked in his breath sharply. "Pah-riss!" he exclaimed. " 'Tis a *terrible* city, I'm told. Everyone drivin' at ninety on the wrong side of the road! And ye didn't get yerself kilt?" He was relieved in a fatherly way to learn that I had never actually driven in Paris. " 'Twas a blessing," he declared. "Now ye'll never run into annything like that in Ireland! 'Tis firm we are about the traffic regulations."

It was wonderful to set out alone on a journey through a country new to me and yet familiar by hearsay, but there was something missing in my feeling of elation. I have never really enjoyed doing anything without a definite objective, and the purpose of travelling merely for pleasure seemed a little empty. As I drove out of County Dublin, heading south and occasionally consulting my map, I apostrophized myself silently. "What do you want now? What are you going to do with yourself?" Freedom, solitude and prosperity were all too new to be comfortable, like clothes newly bought which fit nicely but in which one does not slop around at ease. The sights and sounds, the smells, the colours and the contrasts were too many to allow of serious consecutive thought, and I allowed the hours to pass with my questions unanswered, like the miles of grey road among tweedy patterns.

I spent the night at an inn where I was the only visitor. The wet winter was not conducive to tourism, and I had the place to myself with the exception of an elderly lady of private means who chose to live there all the year round. After an excellent night in a feather-bed (deep down—only my nose sticking out, watching the wobbly candle-flame, feeling like a silk-worm), I sat down to breakfast opposite the old lady. I had to smother a giggle, for she held the *Times* aloft, and I was reminded of all the cartoons I had ever seen as she appeared to eat bacon and eggs, toast and marmalade, somehow *through* the paper, without ever showing her face. I ate, too, with appetite, and then, somewhat sated, began to steal the print as one does in a train, surreptitiously devouring the page facing me. She was immersed in the Births, Marriages and Deaths—or possibly the Personal Columns—so that I was faced with the immutable order of the back page: crossword puzzle and Estate Agents' advertisements. But it was one of those days when most of the ads began: "Licensed Premises." And suddenly, half unbelievingly, I thought: Of course! I shall get a pub—a pub in Ireland. I can buy one now—I can work it. Why not? You don't need special knowledge to serve drinks. Just gumption and energy and good humour. That's it! A pub!" And I laughed out loud, and startled the old lady dreadfully.

Now all that remained was to find it—the pub that was to become a *raison d'être*—and it didn't take very long. Looking for it, wondering at each night-stop whether this wasn't the very place I wanted, each time convinced that no other could be so perfect and yet each time certain that it was not for me, I searched with increasing love and determination until at last my seeking ended where the land did, too: full south.

2 ❧ The Square in Cork

Somewhere along the Kerry-Cork border a subtle change in tempo and tone makes itself felt—a quickening so slight as to be imperceptible unless one is very much in tune. I have never heard anyone say that County Cork is one of Ireland's loveliest, but from the first it affected me more profoundly than the rest.

The bogs are greener, the trees have more personality, the water of the countless rivers, tinged with turf to the pellucid brown of a spaniel's eyes, sings a more rollicking and sometimes a more plaintive tune than the Liffey. The Lee, gathering them together, meanders and hastens in turn towards the great harbour, its tributary, the Owenboy, entering Drake's Pool with some of the elegance that the galleons sheltering there so long ago must have displayed to the round-eyed Corkmen.

Following the rivers through town and village, over grey bridges arched like a well-plucked eyebrow, along fields that sometimes drown in spring floodings, past farm-house and pasture, by tinker encampments and lost little steeples, with the windscreen wipers industriously scrubbing away like tireless charwomen, I came to Cork.

Having grown up in the double loop of the Lee, Cork

has the glamour and the squalor of an ancient Italian city, without the sunshine, but with all the vistas of quays, old stone and astonishing glimpses of pure romantic landscape, sandwiched between mean buildings (with the smells, the raucousness, the gaiety and the distress), muffled yells from back streets, derisive hawking of corner-boys, childhood tears that sound the same in all tongues—and instead of garlic and coffee and sweet peppers the stink of drying hake suspended on nails outside the stores, and with each opening of a tavern door, the sour-sweet assurance of forgetfulness in malt.

Its layout determined by the wilful bends of the river, the city (it has a cathedral, neo-Victorian and quite hideous) has few straight streets and only one wide one of any consequence. This is Patrick Street, falling down the hill from McCurtain (once Queen) Street, tumbling loosely over Patrick's Bridge (where sanctity presumably is cast overboard), walking quite straight with the dignity of the nearly sober for about half a mile, and then, quite overcome, burying its head in the broad transversal lap of the Grand Parade. Here one can turn right or left, but as we are not at present concerned with the full length of the Parade, let us turn right into a small square, a mere slight widening of the road channelled abruptly into three narrow bottle-necks leading away appropriately, one to the hospital, one to a street of sin and pawnshops, and the last to the Coal Quay, which, of course, is not where Cork's coal supply is handled at all.

It is a number of things: meeting place, boxing-ring, dramatic centre, what you will. Mostly it is the general market, black with damp woollen shawls, gay with produce, alive with minor vermin, sonorous with the life and lusts and the lamentations of the people.

The countryside comes there early and leaves late, thirsty without cease, ever ready to postpone the bargain-

ing and the bartering, to hand over a stall or barrow to a neighbour for the time necessary to quench that thirst. The impracticality of the race does not extend to a shortage of public-houses, and in the small square, the appendix of the Patrick Street gut, so to speak, is one of the many inns clustering around this fecund ant-hill of commerce and noisy contention.

It is called Daunt's Square.

When I first arrived in Cork, I was advised to stay at a local temperance hotel, "for sure 'tis the only place ye can be sure of getting a drink—at *any* time." This statement, despite the presence of self-conscious-looking pledge-takers (their loud badges proclaiming their abstemiousness), I found to be strictly true, which in itself is surprising of a Cork statement. Here, and in other places where my letters of introduction took me, I met many and varied types, and quite soon, what with "having an uncle a priest" and a good capacity for liquor, I found all the *petites entrées* were mine for the asking. No one of respectability would be seen using the *grandes entrées* anyway—of which more later.

It may have been any one of a number of things which decided Cork to receive me kindly—a solid Catholic background, an outlandish accent (sounding strange to my own ears among the brogues) or a readily bent elbow. Whatever it was, it worked, and I soon had many acquaintances of good will. I found a surrealist quality about them which, combined with their simplicity and warmth, was irresistibly attractive—a combination like Bovril and Cleopatra.

When it became known, as it very soon did, that I was seeking an alehouse to buy, suggestions came pouring in, and I was taken on the most fantastic pub-crawls of all time. Of these refuges of the thirsty and the sad, the bored and the weary, little can be said that doesn't equally apply to the pub that I was about to own—or rather, to belong to.

It was a three-story building some two or three hundred years old with no architecture and an excellent view of the little *carré*—Daunt's Square—where the annual *Corpus Christi* celebrations were held, rain or shine, but mostly rain.

It had dark brown painted woodwork, innocent of all pretension to oak, and small weak light-bulbs suspended on high. A respectable widow tenanted the top floor, and with her were her two pretty daughters, who happily took after her.

In common with other normal pubs in Eire it had no noticeable conveniences and certainly no one had ever considered installation of one—an odd foreign notion of mine that filled everyone with a blend of pride and alarm. There followed also a veiled doubt about its use, interpreted somewhat loosely during the early days by the constant use of the hose.

Two maiden ladies had inherited the house in the dim days of the "trouble" when their father died in the good cause and an advanced state of intoxication. It had flourished less and less under their teetotal direction, in sympathy with the wizening of their bodies and the slackening of their souls. When at last, exasperated beyond consolation by the whole thing, the elder sister chose to expire, business was bad and the remaining old lady had to soldier along for some years of near-starvation.

When I arrived on the scene she had just decided to get rid of the soul-destroying legacy, and having no idea of modern values put a pitifully low price on it. This I paid with almost indecent haste.

It was what is known as a "free" house. The interpretation to put on this is not the one most laymen give it. A "tied" house can only purchase its wares from one particular brewer or distiller, which has the advantage of particularly good service from the wholesalers in terms of time—and the disadvantage of the contempt bred by familiarity when scarce lines are required.

The reverse is true of the free house, which gets the very best from all the brewers, who naturally want to sell as much of their product as possible and who feel that one brand competing with another in the same bar at the same time must be at its best in order to succeed. The easy-going drinker who has no prejudices usually frequents the free house where he can follow the inclination of the moment and choose his poison without limitations.

There was sawdust on the floor—rather vintage—some dusty brewery advertisements on the walls, and faded cerise curtains inside the front windows. Behind the bar stood three casks of stout, a shelf with fluffy-looking glasses, a large crucifix, and a tall stool, which, as it was waist-high to the old lady, I could only imagine served as an ornament.

In a rack beside the chipped mirror, some bottles of gin and Paddy whisky stood dismally on their heads, accepting in a sort of hopeless inversion the infrequent drains on their resources; an enormous ginger tomcat sat by a grey tea-towel on the end of the counter, bristling at every approach. He was known affectionately as Foxy—the Irish synonym for ginger—and when the time came to get him captured by an R.S.P.C.A. man with a large butterfly net and coils of rope, he lived up to his name. I shall never forget that poor little man belting up and down three flights of stairs and pitting his wits against those of the madder but much more intelligent feline. If the man won in the end, it was not through mental superiority but sheer animal patience, of which the clever cat had none.

One entered the bar proper with the counter stretching along the wall to the left and a low bench running the full length of the room on the right. Here and there kitchen tables, stained the prevalent brown, provided impartial support for drink, drinker and drunk—and some solid stools were at hand should things become a little lively. At the end of the room was an archway and beyond this a larger room with a fireplace opposite the entrance, and an enormous dresser containing the bottles of stout "rising"—of which more later. An occasional mild explosion in this area caused no concern. Here too were benches and kitchen tables, and everywhere the fermenting pungency of stout—flat, medium and high—reminiscent of every fresh and putrefying odour known to nostrils, curiously disgusting and comforting at the same time.

My mind full of check curtains and cosy "bistro's," I stood dreamily visualizing new paint, fresh sawdust and a sink to replace the chipped enamel basin coyly hiding on the counter behind the box for the blind.

You cannot stand dreamily in a pub with empty hands, and small Paddy by small Paddy my ideas grew bigger and rosier, until Mooney's Irish Houses seemed pathetic. The cheque signed, the deeds handed over, I felt the fond hopes of the new mother confronted by a child which, despite all evidence to the contrary, will surely be beautiful some time —its very plainness a guarantee of future charm, a tacit challenge to upbringing.

The pub took me over—that was all there was to it. I don't seem to be explaining why, though—why it should have seized me where all the others had let me slip through their rusty swing doors. I think it was at first the handful of customers who fascinated me, so much so that I couldn't wait to have them to myself and quite begrudged the poor old lady her last few hours of office.

This is more the story of these people—or at least, that part of their story which I knew—than of myself or of the pub we shared. I should like you to meet them by degrees, and see as I did with each new encounter wherein lay the draw, and how inextricably the delightful and the revolting blended in them to produce the most unreal, fairy-tale human individuals—an intrinsic part of a group with no solidarity at all save that of interdependence.

There were only a few of them at first, mostly old, and even in their wilder moments, chained to ancient custom and familiar places, not caring whether their habitual venue was gay or dismal; sufficient for them that it was habitual and therefore comforting.

They were poor for the most part, proud sometimes, cringing and cadging at others. They treated you when they could, scrounged from you when they couldn't, laughed with you and hated you by turns—and sometimes they talked with the tongues of angels, and sometimes they were foul-mouthed. Most often they were taciturn, sad and lonely.

I learned that their homes were usually cramped hovels: the light and warmth of the pub, by contrast, drew them and enwrapped them in temporary comfort so that the daily miseries seemed to dwindle, and they and their thoughts grew fine and large and important. Best of all, others were there to share in this joyous phenomenon.

We grew to each other, I and these people who were my livelihood, at the easy restful pace of a country which should have a cliché for *mañana* or *boukra* but doesn't even bother. From the beginning I knew that I wanted to explore them clinically, to analyse and see what made them tick, and to enjoy their absurdities, be horrified by their rottenness and love passionately the deep beauties they so often succeeded in hiding. What I could not then know was that I should cleave so closely to them that to struggle free I should have to destroy friendship with them—and this I could not have believed.

The first evening of my "take-over" I paid less attention than I should have liked to the mass of my customers —a far greater number than was usual or indeed expected, but Cork is small and parochial and the knowledge of the pub's sale had spread within an hour of the ink's drying on the contract, so that shawlies and corner-boys, grocers and prostitutes, bank clerks and rival publicans flocked to look the new Mrs. over and assess her possibilities in terms of the slate, the Garda and the competition.

Sure they were a gay lot, pleased with a novelty and starting in the right spirit of a solvency which would have surprised a more experienced barkeeper. There is nothing haphazard about the methods of the Irish toper—he plays mine host as an accomplished angler plays his fish. Credit is seldom asked for—it is sometimes given, grudgingly perhaps, but usually volunteered when the innkeeper has been manoeuvred into an untenable position and face must be saved.

On this night, the atmosphere was like that of a homecoming of a novel kind: the exuberance of the welcome, the excitement in the air mingled with the smell of wet wool and rubber, fish, drink, smoke and of course sweat, to create a euphoria amounting almost to intoxication, although I drank nothing. This was because I was too busy and would certainly have had far too many had I started. It is customary to give "one on the house" on taking over, and all the guests wanted to reciprocate.

The stream of names, even more confusing than at a conventional cocktail party, slurred softly into what sounded like a Gaelic chant or the legends of the Bards—O'Learys, Kelleghers, Morans, MacInerneys, Connollys and O'Connells—with an occasional memorable Smith or Brown (obvious legacies of the hated tyrant, but well assimilated and neutralized by a protective Tadg or Sean or Patrick).

Most knew each other well, others knew of each other,

so that it was not unlike a family reunion—nearly everyone had mutual relations, or at least relations who had blown up a mutual bridge whilst in the I.R.A. or shared a bomber whilst in the R.A.F. The atmosphere was one of cordiality and liking—and at least initially there were no silences, and no apparent antagonisms.

I noticed a thin, rather stooped man who leaned over the end of the counter near the Murphy barrel. He looked strange, partly because he was drinking a whisky and soda. He said nothing, but looked around him calmly, smiling at this one and that and raising his hand occasionally in greeting to some customer separated from him by the crowd. His gaze rested briefly on all of them, and I fancied that at one point it focused on me a fraction of a moment longer.

He was about forty, with lovely strong bones to his face which, however, had a certain curious incompleteness—disconcerting. It was a face which should have been passionate, experienced, bearing the evidence of adventure and hardship, of physical and spiritual storms, but looked as though these had been seen from a distance, longed for, perhaps even understood but never quite felt: an emptiness not frustrated but aware and a little bitter.

As I polished glasses, poured pints, made change and polite conversation, these thoughts flicked inconsequentially through my mind, and I raised my eyes again to see something that pleased me unreasonably. There was no trace of cynicism in the half-smile at the corners of his eyes—instead, what I described to myself as an almost angelic quality. His features were those one associates automatically with the Irish: black hair, blue eyes, a faintly snub nose and a wide humorous mouth. Two less conventional details arrested my attention: outward-rising eyebrows with a satanic peak to them, and two deep strong lines pulling down the

24

corners of the mouth, not sulkily but with unconscious sadness.

He wore a fisherman's sweater and corduroys, a Jaeger scarf, and he might have been a porter or a peer. I thought through the bustle of concentration and the garishness of the scene that he could be a man to love greatly, and forgot all about him in the next moment.

The feeling had no chance to become more than half-conscious, for just as my stomach-muscles tightened with the thought, a carter from Upton became drunk.

He did this with the suddenness of three hours of accumulated stout going off like dynamite. With quiet dignity he stood up and unbuckled the wide leather belt that appeared to support his trousers, which, however, stayed up as the blond giant whirled the heavy strap around his head —the enormous metal buckle singing viciously through the air and stirring the smoke into wisps, while the crowd moved apart in the measured way of familiarity.

I had no experience of this sort of thing and was seized with a longing for the sunlit terrace of some quiet café with a cool drink and no worries—but there was nothing for it.

Keeping as low as I could below the menacing arc of the buckle, I approached, took an enormous breath and said, very loudly and firmly, the first thing that came into my head (offensively French):

"Espèce d'imbécile—fous le camp!"

There was a deathly hush as the belt fell to the floor and the lad crossed himself hastily, his example followed immediately by the whole crowd.

A doubt was growing which I hastened to dispel by asking whether the carter would have "one on the house." A sigh of relief was audible throughout the room. Whatever spell or incantation I had uttered, it could not be evil,

25

for what witch would do the gentlemanly thing so promptly? Over his final pot, drunk slowly and cautiously, the lad confessed that he was so fed up with being kind to "them horses. that sure sometimes I just have to take a swing at something—and sure, Mrs. O', I'd not be after trying to hit anything but the air!"

Not for the first time that evening, I was struck by this curious form of address—"Mrs. O'." Why was I Mrs. O'? Or maybe they spelt it Mrs. Owe? Or OH! It wasn't even the initial of my name, which in any case I shouldn't have expected more than one or two to know. At the time, I had no chance to inquire, but later I learned that it was one of those remarkable manifestations of the innate courtesy and politeness of the Irish. The lowliest of corner-boys knows that "Mrs." is offensive in the vocative unless accompanied by a name. If this latter is missing, sure you get as near to it as you can by making a likely noise: obviously in Ireland, the most likely would begin with a clear and distinct "O." As long as I was in Ireland, I remained Mrs. O' to friends and familiars—but the thing that still puzzles me is that throughout that time I never heard anyone else addressed so. I felt that it was somehow my own title—in a personal and endearing way.

Whilst Mike had been doing his parlour-trick, Mrs. Flannigan had been doing hers. This well-known figure from the Coal Quay was to give me plenty of headaches and memories, but of this I was still blissfully ignorant. The women of Southern Ireland, with particular reference to Cork, wear black woollen shawls for warmth and because, as the Irish share a passion for mourning with the other Catholic races of more temperate climes, black is the most durable colour. In the vernacular, these women are known as shawlies, and they have an excellent use for their distinguishing garment apart from the purely utilitarian one of warmth and protection from the elements. Look at it this way—if you are wrapped up in something rather shapeless and opaque, what can't you hide under it?

In the case of my shawlies, glasses, preferably the large one-and-sixpenny size, were the object of their favour, and it was necessary to keep a sharp eye on the number of "pots" issued. This, of course, I didn't know yet, but poor Mrs. Flannigan had done well with the Guinness, and was not quite steady on her feet as she rose from the bench where she had spent most of the evening. As she rose, she clanked. Two other customers, out to prove beyond doubt their loyalty to the house (as a basis for tick or odd jobs), drew my attention to the clanking which was certainly incompatible with Mrs. Flannigan's roly-poly physique. What to do?

The feel of the land was creeping into me, and I hastened to help the old woman to steady herself—and then: "Mrs. Flannigan," said I, "can I help you with your glasses?"

This was dead-pan stuff, but it went over in a big way.

Dropping two in her amusement, she handed over four, roaring with laughter, the while other ladies in the same costume were seen to turn their backs briefly, and the tables were suddenly covered with empty glasses.

That night there were no more problems of any seriousness, and when the last Guard had left at three o'clock, I locked up and stepped wearily into the car, full of a good feeling.

It was very dark and the rain had stopped for a catnap: my tyres sizzled gently along the black satin ribbon of road, polka-dotted with shiny acetylene reflections—no lights shone in the houses.

As I prepared for bed, my mind hummed with tired half-thoughts. (Another night—another pub—very late and the Garda coming in to claim the normal thirty pieces of silver, the free drink entitling longer hours. Among the four policemen was a new broom, sweeping, if not clean, very thoroughly. Sure and he took everyone's particulars, his small whisky in his right hand and his Biro in his left, and his attention was suddenly drawn to Father Murphy, who was with the gentry.

"Are ye a traveller, Father?" he inquired in the accepted form.

"I am that," responded the priest.

"And where did ye sleep last night?" Also according to the time-honoured formula.

One of the Padre's companions, without hesitation, answered for him: "Sure, Officer, do ye not know that the good Father here has so many worries and responsibilities on his mind that he *could* not sleep last night?"

"Yerrah, 'tis true," said the Guard. "I'd not be adding to your troubles, Father."

Established as a bona-fide traveller, and therefore entitled to drink after hours, the priest waxed hospitable and the thirsty Garda were rewarded for their forbearance.)

I brushed my hair before the mirror and had to laugh quietly, for I had raised the corners of my eyebrows and pulled my mouth down in the unconscious travesty of a more recent memory.

3 ⁂ Phelan

Tonight I feel a malaise all the more irritating as
t is without pain and without reason. Small problems assume an undeserved importance in a mind that feels stale
and the greater sadnesses that keep so quiet in their accustomed durance are looking out now—tentatively still, but I
know of their stirring. This is not one of the nights when a
brisk walk, a hot bath and a pile of books can restore ease
and serenity.

I light the candles, build a roaring fire, pour myself a
large drink with every intention of repeating it, and here I
am. Well, here I am and what of it? Ah, yes, the joss-sticks—
I had forgotten those, and a packet of Gauloises. Really,
if all else fails, who could avoid loosening up and yielding
to memories and regrets, absurd hopes and relaxed accept-
ances, with the pure sensual pleasure of this rough, vicious
tobacco in their lungs?

Again memory and recalled emotion seem to respond
to an olfactory impulse. This time my nose is leading me
back to an experience framed in cheap pipe tobacco, wet earth
and cowpats—with no peat fires, no cooking smells and no
green things growing. Also, yes, a faint acid undertow of
misery translated through clammy, consumptive sweat.

It was some days after my accession to the duck-board that Phelan came in. He was far more like my idea of a Welsh miner than an Irish burglar, but I had no reason to doubt what he himself told me and my customers chattily confirmed. If you can believe that he looked like a miner—assuming you have a mental image of such—I need add nothing descriptive except to say that he was not, of course covered in coal-dust.

"Yerrah, 'tis an honest man is Phelan," they said. "Fifteen separate convictions he's after having—and never robbed a person at all!"

He was a sort of Robin Hood of burglars; he and his family, which was painfully large, were of course extremely poor, and on their behalf he systematically robbed the rich—but always in the collective singular. His particular morality lay in the belief that a large firm, preferably ending "& Co.," was fair game inasmuch as no single individual owned the goods he stole, therefore he hurt nobody, which his gentle soul would have abhorred.

He was not a very clever burglar, being self-taught which as any specialist will tell you is just not good enough. For this reason he kept getting caught and was as familiar with the inside of the city jail as he was with his own room in which nine fretful little palefaces shared with a beautiful skeleton of a mother a penury so seldom relieved that a spoonful of margarine or a piece of dried fish quite upset them.

The tuberculosis to which the family was subject had already claimed four of the sickly brood. Now it was a gruesome and terrifying race: Would it take another child, beloved, precious and desperately expensive—or would it first take the father or the mother, leaving the children to a speedier death, untinged by haemorrhage or pain?

It was May when I met Phelan. One of the corner

oys that hung around my horseshoe-curve of pavement had eceived an absurdly large tip from an American of Irish ntecedents, and he wished to prove equally generous, inviting the burglar to join him in my pub.

Phelan, whom I grew to love very quickly as a human eing and as a kind of warped saint, could never make his areer pay to the extent of buying himself more than a pot r two a month; he was no scrounger, but he drank many ree drinks—and in this connection I noted with pleasure hat the friends and well-wishers who offered him hospitaly were all nearly as destitute as he was.

This particular night, he was in wonderful form. A epartment store in the fashionable Prince's Street area had roved to contain a splendid and easily concealed haul, and is family had eaten, his wife had smiled, and young Tom ad had a delicately fringed white armband of the purest lk for his First Holy Communion. The unspeakable joy f being able to offer the good Father a cup of tea and a lice of cake when he called on this occasion! Phelan was light with contentment; he vibrated with unfamiliar happiness; he smiled with the expression of a baby holding a ainbow.

A story of the fooling of an English officer during the roubled years amused him beyond measure. He laughed xcessively and coughed. . . . Again he coughed, and the haki rag he wore, ironically, up his cuff, began to sport usset patches—and I threw a little Lysol into the washing-up vater when his glass grew empty.

I was not to see him again for some weeks, and when e came back, he was still basking in comparative luxury. Three minor burglaries had remained undiscovered (I like o believe that the Garda, too, are charitable), and the Phelan amily was savouring unaccustomed freedom from utter vant.

He talked to me in the easy comfortable way that onl publicans hear—confessions too deep for the confessiona even in a land where this particular form of self-liberatio is as natural as breathing. His talk was lovely with the sof ness of the brogue and the sincerity of the feeling. H spoke of the profound tenderness he felt for his wife, whicl as he put it, "makes me love her so hard, that God save u I can't help it, Mrs. O'—and she—she feels the same. . . .

He described the darling beauty of each new baby— sliding gently, yet to him quite perceptibly along the hu: gry slope to annihilation. He told me of the terror th; each law-breaking poured into his marrow and, indirectly, c the sublime courage each repeated petty crime required.

"Jesus God, if only there was work for the likes c me!" His eyes were eager and tragic.

"Can ye just dream," he exclaimed, "of two rooms an a bit of earth to grow praties and cabbages for the litt] ones. . . ."

Because I wanted to know him well, because I had deep admiration for his courage in his weakness, I aske him often to drink as a guest of the house—which I had t do with infinite tact, for as I said before, he was no scrounge:

And then, one night it was dark and very cold—an the frost was on everything and almost in one's heart— dried-up with an unpleasing suddenness from the accu; tomed mosquito net of drizzle.

I was alone behind the counter, having given my ba: maid, Bridie, the evening off to get herself a "pairmanent."

Phelan walked in quietly, came up to the bar where h laid his head on his arms and cried as I have never see anyone cry—and God save us never hope to again.

It is always embarrassing to witness deep emotion— in our odd foreshortened attitude to life, the display c despair is considered unseemly—but my concern and affe ion for the poor man were so great and my own emotions so deeply stirred, that I ducked under the hatch and, coming up to him, took his hand and held it tightly in an attempt to convey the sympathy I couldn't express.

"Phelan, boy," I said, "what is it at all?"—noticing gratefully that I had used an Irish turn of phrase—I might not sound too strange and foreign to him in his loneliness.

As though he felt this warmth and welcomed it through the agony of his heart, he spoke heavily through great choking sobs, and I curled up inside with horror which he must not see.

"Ye remember me twins, Mrs. O'? De boy died early his morning and I was after getting a small box for him. Tis ten miles to the simmitry as ye know, but praying a little to our Lady to watch over the child, I took him there on me shoulder. Sure, 'twas broken me heart was—but God save him, he had a dacent burial—the good Father was here. . . ."

He wept now so deeply, from his guts, that regardless of mascara and trade, I wept, too—sharing those moments of sheer spiritual pain magically transformed into bearable physical grief.

"Phelan, boy," I gulped, "be happy that the child is in no pain and has God to look after him now. . . ."

It is horrible to feel that the expression of one's disbeliefs can be of genuine comfort to others. Yet at the time I felt no guilt in this hypocrisy—only the longing to help and to console, no matter how falsely.

"I went back, Mrs. O'," he went on, "and the girl twin had died while I buried the brother. Ah, Holy Mother, I could not stand it. Sure, there was no box for this one, and no money to buy one, and 'twas in my arms I took her the last ten miles to join her twin. Father Murphy came again in the buggy, Mrs. O'. 'Twas good of him. Then I came

33

home, and Maggie was there, and she so lovely and s
sad. . . ."

"Phelan," I said, "drink this."

It was straight whisky, up to the rim of a pint pot. I
ever a man needed a swift anaesthetic. . . . He drained i
gave a blank tortured look, like a cow in labour, devoid c
reason and with all the feeling in the world, and then h
said: "Mrs. O', she was so lovely, and 'twas broke entirel
our hearts were. . . . There will be more Phelans to die—
and 'tis I—I'm making them for death. . . ."

He keeled over and I laid him with much effort on
bench; later Sergeant Rooney of the Guards took him home
and the other men helped, too.

I sit here now with the fire turning my legs to pink
veined marble, the good whisky dispersing my own di
comforts and those far-off hurts losing their sharpness in th
French-grey mist of smoke. The joss-sticks are nearly ended
small determined sparks still clinging to them.

The uneasiness has gone, and the revival of an ancien
alien agony which I shared a little, only serves to heighte
my *bien-être*. I am amazed at the remoteness of those rea
days, coloured so fictionally by the fantasy of leaf-coloure
spectacles. I am so glad to find them easy to return to whe
in need, and I enjoy the ever-echoing impact of the weird
ness, the soul-purging ugliness and simplicity and the class
ical drama of that Irish life.

Can one fail to see the utter necessity of superstitio
and ritual in circumstances like those of Phelan? Hatin
the falsity of the philosophy and the cruelty of its grip o
these unfortunates, one can yet have no doubt of its ef
ficiency as a drug. And I would not deny morphia to a ma
in pain even though it destroy him.

4 ❧ ". . . and chronicle small beer." SHAKESPEARE

It didn't take very long to learn the pub business as such. Within a couple of weeks I felt quite competent to serve, to order stock, to do the fairly simple accounting involved, in short to attend to the routine business of the trade as it exists, for instance, in England.

I knew already of many tricks of the trade, and of the fierce competition between the buyer and the seller in the drinking game. I had seen the little bulbous measures into which the up-ended bottles gurgle the appointed tot. Yes, but supposing its transparent depths should have received a preliminary tea-spoonful, say, of some invisible substance like hard glue? A few drops less per tot is a few tots more per bottle. The counter-attack? Every drink in the same glass: the cumulative film of five or six gins in one container adds up to nearly a whole one. There will probably never be a definitive judgment on whether it pays or doesn't to be slightly mean with each measure. A really good barman can appear to be over-lavish as he pours into the little metal goblets, when he is really salting away a nip or two. Conversely, the careful publican may seem cheese-paring when giving scrupulously honest measure. The serving of beer almost any kind of beer, can be regarded in the same way. Conscious control of the operation, born of long experience and the skill that stems therefrom, may mean quite considerable savings for the publican. But there again, it's more important to give the customer less beer and more froth i: he likes it that way. The good bartender soon finds out. The height of "de collar on de old corduroy" was a matter o: prime seriousness to my customers who drank stout—and i was folly to give a ribbed glass to those who liked a plain one, or a tankard to the thin-glass brigade. Anyone in the trade will confirm that drinking idiosyncrasies are more general and less varied than one would believe. There is the man, for instance, who intends to drink two pints. He knows it, and the publican knows it, too. But it must be four half pints if he is to be pleased. Or the old lady, who loves a small port between jobs, but insists on calling it dry sherry. which she wouldn't drink if you served it (as you certainly would the first time!). Or—but perhaps this one is a little too tall—the man who orders three Martinis, and leaves the first "because the first one always tastes so awful!"

Of course, anyone out to cheat in the pub game can do it easily, but the owners who do are few and far between, for somehow, no matter how innocent he may appear, the twister is always identified quite easily by the infallible nose of the regular, who is the backbone of the trade. "No, there's nothing wrong with the 'Ball and Chain,'" he'll tell you, "I just like the 'Anchor' better. It feels more . . . comfortable, y'know?" And the short measure flourishes only in those great bars where thousands flow through daily, never to return: railway refreshment rooms, "smart" bars on elegant thoroughfares, anywhere where the trade is "passing." It won't do for regulars. Any more than the many undetectable little tricks like slightly adulterated gin (hard to spot—very—a tot or two of plain alcohol in twenty-three of gin! and the drink no less potent) or a few measures of cheaper whisky in a bottle of the best. Especially as these doctored drinks are normally reserved for the second or third round, when palates are a little blunted, and spirits, in every sense, high. But there are all the endearing little habits of the client, too, to set against this somewhat dismal picture. One never seems to think of the man who coughs all over the counter, the one who hasn't washed for weeks, the tearful, the bellicose, the garrulous: all deterrents to the good customer, real threats to a publican's daily trade. One bum leaning on a counter can mean the loss of an hour's good business. I used to wonder at the strictures on prostitutes in many bars until I had one of my own. In Australia, no respectable woman will go to a bar counter unless accompanied by a man, and those who do are seldom served. It is assumed they are there to solicit, and that, too, interferes with the calm drinking-pleasure of the respectable customer. These were all small things, many of which I already knew, but, in the running of a bar in Ireland, there are pitfalls for the rash or unwary of which I had not dreamed when making my plans. One of the first moments of panic that beset me came early, soon after I had started trading.

The brewery had delivered the two casks I had ordered on the advice of Bridie, in whose experience as a barmaid I had a touching faith. One flat, one high, she told me, and they came; we needed high stout at the time. You blend high and flat to avoid excessive frothing. But although we had the casks, we did not have the stout, for when I told Bridie to get on with it and open the thing, she raised her hands in horror. "Yerrah, Mrs. O'—I couldn't tap a barrel! I've never tapped one in me life!"

37

That made two of us, and I was nonplussed. It occurred to me, and grateful I am that it did, that amateur tapping of high stout might lead to trouble. I ran across the road and, turning into the Coal Quay, I made for the nearest rival establishment. The proprietor was a large "foxy" fellow, his nose almost as red as his hair, and he looked a tough customer.

Rather hesitantly, I asked him whether he would tap my barrel. He laughed loudly and consented, but, as we crossed the road together, he asked me why I hadn't made the carters do the job. Apparently they were supposed to, but didn't unless one had the forethought to offer them a drink.

I watched the man carefully and when he had done the job and the small trickle of froth from the rim of the bung-hole had subsided, I thanked him and said, "Now that I know how, I shan't have to bother you again."

He looked down incredulously at my five-foot-three of skin and bone and said shortly, "Don't be a fool, girl. Yerrah, if ye don't get the tap in right, ye'll have Guinness on the ceiling and yerself in hospital!" and he stalked out.

For some absurdly childish reason, this infuriated me and I determined to tap the next barrel if it killed me. I had really watched most carefully and knew that if I could only hit hard enough on the third blow, it would be all right. I surveyed the mallet thoughtfully. It was a large block of wood with a short handle. If the handle were longer, I could hit harder but much more slowly . . . that was no good. But if the head of the mallet were heavier, that might make the short swing just as effective.

I had recently discovered a huge horseshoe under the counter and had not yet got around to throwing it out. This I bound to the back of the mallet-head, and the added weight felt good in my fist.

Bridie was out when the next consignment was delivered and only Mrs. Flannigan and a couple of her cronies sat on the long bench, tippling their way placidly through the dull morning.

The carters in a great hurry put the cask in its place and rushed off: I was faced with a dusty bung, some newspaper and the brass tap. Had Mrs. Flannigan not been there, I might have weakened, but her presence strengthened my resolve and, taking a deep breath, I marched behind the counter and fetched my reinforced mallet. Wrapping the barrel end of the tap in three thicknessess of newspaper as I had seen Foxy do, I placed the tap against the bung, raised the mallet, and thinking briefly that I should probably be the first foreigner ever to be killed by Guinness, I hit the tap two quick fairly light blows. At the second there was a faint sizzling noise and the froth began to ooze around the rim of the bung. That was the critical moment when hesitation or undue haste could produce a nasty explosion. I walloped that tap with all the strength I had, squarely on the head, and the darling thing shot straight into place, firmly and beautifully, the newspaper sealing the infinitesimal crack around it. Another light knock and all was safe and secure.

Nonchalantly, I wiped my hands on the back of my capacious apron and strolled behind the counter.

Mrs. Flannigan and the other shawlies were on their feet, their glasses half-way to their open mouths, and I felt that they were about to cross themselves, so I began washing glasses and whistling "Hullo, Patsy Fagan," a piece of New York nonsense which had endeared itself to Cork through its fulsome lyrics and cheerful if hackneyed tune.

By the time we had opened again in the afternoon, after the "Holy Hour," the Coal Quay knew of my feat and the tale of my derring-do joined the drinking legends of Cork. This was splendid, for I told no one about the hastily removed horseshoe and my customers felt that a woman who could tap a high barrel was not to be trifled with and certainly needed no bouncer.

However, inwardly convinced that it had been a glorious fluke like holing out in one, I invariably let the carters do the job after that, watching them with the calm critical look of the professional, and graciously handing out the good free pints as though I were doing them a favour by allowing them to perform an operation of which I could really have made a better job.

But there was still so much to learn! Port was a "small woine." A "seven" was a pint of draught stout (at seven pence). It was a solecism to call a female customer "Madam." You could not, without giving offence, say "Time, gentlemen, please!" Like Edwardian dandies (so help me, long before my time!), the few who fancied soda-water alluded to it as a "splash." I made innumerable mistakes at first, misunderstood orders time and again, and was saved from total disgrace only by my readiness to laugh at my own stupidities. I found this to be, quite unintentionally, the key to my customers' affections: and sometimes, I admit, when things were slow and I felt the atmosphere needed a shot of something, I would deliberately clown a little, my foolishness brightening every face around the bar. Or, if it seemed more appropriate, I would become helpless—an age-old female wile which often stood me in good stead. In all fairness, I must confess that there were always willing hands to assist with any jobs that I couldn't manage alone, and when it was known that I wanted anything done, the next moment the place was alive with experts.

Most of these, of course, were amateur experts, for although there are many skilled men in Eire, employed by big concerns like FORD's, most of them go to England, to towns like Dagenham which are purely Irish in population, and where the pay is good and the work plentiful.

I remember the visit I paid to this grimy outer suburb of London. In some peculiarly homogeneous way—irrefutable argument in favour of mutual colonization—the totally Irish nature and traditions of the people seemed to have fused completely with the native Anglo-Saxon, so that such anomalies were encountered as the superb transport, road, municipal and health services of Britain (lavatories that functioned with magical regularity, immersion heaters, X-ray examinations) and the customs that go with these softening influences: Sunday joints, weeding the garden—in short, gentility—inextricably bound up with wakes, fairies, ceilidh dances, pigs' "croubheens," and the Irish pub.

There was no shortage of hostelries in Dagenham, and when I was taken along by my friends who lived there, I was amused because it might have been anywhere in Ireland. Not a single note of Cockney disturbed the music of assorted brogues. All were drinking stout or Irish whisky, and the talk was of nothing but events of the community itself, or in Eire. Even hats, good English velours and cloches, so dear to the British housewife, yielded pride of place to scarves (colleen-tied under the chin) and peaked caps.

The weather itself seemed characteristic in a smoked-up way, and one had to concentrate on Belisha beacons and the illuminated destinations on buses, to look for the Underground Station to remind oneself that one was really "over."

Dagenham is basically FORD's but I learned in Cork that when the great magnate (who started life as an egg-pedlar in the Clonakilty parish) decided to launch forth in Europe, the first factory he built outside the U.S.A. was the one at Cork (purely an assembly plant). Dagenham, where there are surely more Corkmen employed, came much later.

The skilled workmen who remain in Ireland—despite the lure of the rich life across the water—have more often than not succumbed to the easy-going slovenly ways that the island breeds so insidiously in the moist silver-grey atmosphere, where sounds are sweeter for being gently muffled and the slow drizzle seems to reprove haste and urgency.

A few there are, however, who have the skills but use them seldom—fallen below themselves perhaps through drink, or laziness or misfortune. I met such a one when a fuse went just as evening was beginning to sweep the last dust of day out through my back door. My violent exclamation of disgust drew the attention of a thin-chested, lanky individual with bushy hair, merry eyes and crooked stained teeth. He came up to me, grinning. " 'Tis only a fuse," he said. "I'll be after fixing it for ye."

He did this, and in our subsequent conversation I learned—for he was not humble—that he was an excellent electrician. He comes into this story several times, so I shall not say here all that I knew about him. Let me just introduce him: Paddy Donovan, skilled tradesman, gifted story-teller, talented liar, intermittent pledge-taker, occasional thief and champion drunkard. He was well educated and his wife, who had also been well educated, was beautiful and unhappy in her devotion to him. They had four children and no luck. He became a great friend of mine, and a frequent headache. I cannot imagine Cork without him, and indeed, he is still there, under four feet of the earth St. Patrick made barren of snakes.

That was for me a memorable night, for as the lights came on again and my spirits brightened with them, the door swung open and the lovely man who had stirred me on my first evening in the pub, entered and gave me the smile you keep for friends and familiars. I returned it and felt the maddening blush which still comes sometimes when it is aparently least justified. Something about him plunged me back into a night in a small pub further north: the daughter of the house, painfully beautiful with horrible red hands and piano legs, singing in a small flat voice the ballads of an ancient and tortured race—hurting immensely through the heart whilst mildly offending the ear, accompanied by a raucous instrument aptly dubbed "the gadget." Her parents, full of an unwonted greed, trying with all their wiles and guts to keep a spoiled local rabble under control, to convey good fellowship, to show what a "good" business it was to run. And in the faces of the men listening to the minor keys and the broad vowels, I saw the incompleteness, the desire that only those who live in unnatural chastity with the Damocles' sword of retribution suspended over them can show so clearly in almost saintly features, that it becomes an obsession canalized into Stout. Then I learned of the poverty and obedience that compelled these people to await fulfilment until they could afford marriage—the delayed matings that ended so often in quiet undramatic disaster. Why? I wondered. . . .

"Good evening," he said, with the end of the smile wrapped around the words.

I gave him back the greeting and raised my eyebrows in a query. Somehow I didn't want to ask the standard question: "What will it be?" or "What can I be getting ye?" that runs so easily off the tongue for the "regulars." I knew he wanted a Scotch and soda—and how could I let him know that I remembered this from a busy crowded night?

He asked for it quietly and offered me a cigarette. As he lit it for me, I saw his hands—short, strong, stubby fingers with broad, fleshy palms—their very white backs softened with tiny curling black hairs.

He didn't smell of Cork—his aura was of good tobacco and shaving-cream and the faint smell of fresh perspiration.

43

There were few customers, all seated on the benches, for it was early yet and the men were home having their "tea": I wanted badly to talk to him and even more urgently to hear him talk, but some unaccustomed instinct of caution made me leave that end of the bar and busy myself with the small meaningless tasks of the hands that leave the mind free to wander.

He sat on one of the tall dark stools I had just bought and which the custom regarded as extremely grand. I polished an already gleaming glass with absurd energy and he grinned.

"Would that one be for Mrs. Flannigan, now?" he asked, and the memory of my little brush with that good lady made me laugh: at once everything felt comfortable and the tight feeling round my heart disappeared.

I was absurdly happy and the emotion he aroused in me felt both natural and deeply satisfying. We talked lightly and pleasantly, and I was amazed at his knowledge of the Coal Quay and its denizens, for he was clearly not of them, nor, to my mind, did he even sound like a Corkman.

My own brogue was coming on apace, for I am vulnerable to accents and intonations, and I made no effort to resist the music of the language.

"You're not a Corkwoman, are you? Is it Clare you come from?"

I defied him to guess my birthplace and he ranged over the British Isles and the Empire, making wilder and funnier guesses. As he talked gaily, I studied his voice and his mannerisms. Certainly he was Irish, but I couldn't place him at all. He conveyed the impression of gentle birth without the routine expressions and catch-phrases of the public-school man.

At last I said, "Surely you lose, now; you've had far

more than twenty questions. Now it's my turn. Are you from Dublin?"

The smile left his face and the uplifted eyebrows looked almost menacing.

"It is of no consequence where I come from," he answered formally, and it felt like a slap in the face.

Unwilling to show my hurt, I shrugged my shoulders, and at once his eyes lit up. His mouth widened and showed great square white teeth and, with this lightning change of expression he clapped his hand to his forehead and said, "I'm getting slow in my old age! That's a continental shrug —and me taking you for an Irishwoman or one of His Majesty's subjects! You'd think I'd never strayed beyond Upton!"

I laughed. It was impossible to stay angry with this odd creature who made my hands tremble and my muscles go taut.

For a little longer we made cheerful impersonal conversation, conducted in the easy manner of chance acquaintances on a bus, who will never meet again. Then he paid for his drink and, bidding me good night in French with a good accent, he left.

The fuggy beer-smelling pub put its arms around me and squeezed me back into my publican's body.

Looking around me, I saw the shabbiness and the drear of the place with a new awareness; suddenly it came over me with intense urgency that it was time to do something about it.

Paddy Donovan was still in the bar and I called him over to ask whether the wiring of the house would stand more and better lights. He was emphatic that it would not. Contemptuously, he pointed out the age of the makeshift paraphernalia of wires and plugs.

" 'Tis rewiring entirely it needs, Mrs. O'," he said.

45

"And I'm the boyo to do it for ye. Leave me to get the stuff, and I'll start in the morning."

"Wait a minute, Paddy—what will it cost?"

"Yerrah, don't worry about that, Mrs. O'. Sure ye'd have to get it done within the year anyway. I can get most of the stuff at trade," he added, winking, "and all I'll need to start with will be a small advance from ye."

It transpired that the small advance was needed to get his tools out of pawn, where they went regularly at the onset of his drinking bouts—from one of which he had just emerged. Ten days of continuous drinking: truly remarkable, even in Cork! He was still a little shaky but it was common knowledge that between sprees he hardly drank at all, so that there should be several weeks in hand of virtual sobriety. Mentally I calculated that the wiring job couldn't take that long.

We agreed as to the smallness of the advance, and it was decided that he would indeed "start in the morning."

When he had gone, another project occurred to me—suggested by the prosaic fact that a back alley marked my southern boundary—and for the rest of the evening I worked with only half my attention on the job.

I think I mentioned earlier the Corkonian predilection for the *petites entrées*. Although there is scarcely a successful man in Ireland who does not drink, there is a cosy convention that places him above reproach in all respects including that one (possibly some hangover of "virtue is its own reward"—ergo the rewarded are virtuous), therefore it follows that he should not be seen entering a bar. That he should be seen inside one, in the company of his peers or clients, does not seem to confuse anyone: it is a contradiction of the sort which delights the Irish, who derive huge enjoyment from the bewilderment of the foreigner.

As a result of this, any tavern patronized by the more

prosperous has a back or side entrance situated as inconspicuously as location permits and adjacent to a back stairway. The respectable can thus use the *petite entrée* and avoid the vulgar publicity of the *grande*.

I thought with satisfaction of the empty first floor over the bar, the stairway with the back door beside it, and the blissful anonymity of the unlighted lane which was used as a short cut by everyone with business in the city and which could therefore be explained away easily by anyone meeting an awkward acquaintance there. In the lane, too, were the "conveniences"—an added incentive to those who would remain unnoticed.

I could see no flaw in the facilities at my disposal, and determined then and there to open a cocktail bar on the first floor. With Paddy already doing one job on the premises, and other workmen to follow in his traces anyway, the opportunity was too good to be missed.

Mentally I plunged into a delicious welter of colour schemes, lighting, materials, in the wholly feminine delight of "doing up" a room.

That it would be an investment costing money and requiring careful planning in order to prove profitable, I knew. That it would be a success I had no doubt at all—wishful thinking perhaps, or may be a preliminary flicker of "the sight"?

It had been a good day—in parts a lovely day—and full of my hopeful plans, I went gaily home at a late hour, with other almost unconscious hopes contributing to my sense of joyous anticipation.

5 ❧ The New Bar and Daisy

With the rewiring for the new lights, a busy time started. Paddy Donovan was in his element, rushing around between ceilings and beams, coils of flex dangling crazily from his pockets, his tools scattering around him in joyous clatter, sparks emerging from unlikely places and yards of what he called "con-doo-it" tripping everyone up.

Why he was never electrocuted I shall never know: I would not have changed places with his guardian angel. From the bottom of ladders I would cry anxiously, "Paddy, is that wire alive?"

"I'll just see," he'd say, seizing it in a grimy paw.

Sometimes it was and sometimes it wasn't. I took his word for it, but made sure that the pub carried a good third-party insurance.

The decision to leave the downstairs bar basically unaltered was one which I made after a good deal of thought, and when the freshening-up was over, I was glad that I hadn't done anything drastic.

It kept its personality but lost the gloom of dirt and darkness. The plummy cerise curtains went, and in their place hung pleasant, rough, nubbly folkweave, unpretentious, cheerful, and above all, clean. The glass frills dangling from the ceilings, doing their best to hide the dim winking of forty watts beneath them, went, too—and in their place we had some plain semi-concealed fittings with strong bulbs inside. All the brown varnish was stripped and the natural wood allowed to look old and weathered under a light coat of wax.

Paddy, who, by virtue of being my first assistant in the conversion of the pub, had assumed the status of adviser, hirer of other labour, general factotum and public nuisance, tackled me firmly about the fireplace.

"Terrazzo is what ye want, Mrs. O'," he said. " 'Tis all the rage."

I knew it was. Cork had broken out in a rash of dull-coloured marble chips. Floors, bathrooms, tiles—all looking like *pointilliste* jig-saw puzzles conceived by a mind unhinged and sunk in gloom—were everywhere.

The fireplace was enormous, well shaped in the farmhouse tradition, and covered with plaster painted the blue you see around Moslem windows, daubed on with the intention of keeping the *afrits* away.

To Paddy's disgust and shame, when I had had all this muck scraped off and the bricks freshened to their own warm glow, I obtained a solid wrought-iron fender, as plain as I could find, put two sturdy benches either side of it, and was satisfied.

The floors had grown quite used to regular scrubbing now and felt good underfoot, with the fresh sawdust forever shifting into new patterns like small deserts windswept into curls and squiggles.

Only the colossal dresser remained a problem—its precious freight homeless if I scrapped it. The day they scraped the plaster off the fireplace, fate took a hand.

Whether the unaccustomed banging and vibration were too much for it, or whether in my artistic fervour I had left the stout bottles to rise a day or so longer than they needed, I don't know, but suddenly there was a noise like a bomb, and froth and brown liquid everywhere—half the dresser still stood and the other half was ready-chopped firewood for a month. Nobody was hurt, and we removed the few remaining bottles to safety. Then, with a sigh of pleasure, I assisted in the total demolition of the hideous object.

"And where," said Paddy, in the tone of one who propounds an unanswerable conundrum, "will ye be after keeping the bottled stuff now?"

There was a small outhouse which I had used as a store for empty crates and soft drinks. There, when not in use, sat the Crown corking machine—for few self-respecting publicans get their bottled stout from the brewery. It is in bottling your own—a process which has its amusing side —that you make your real profit.

"Could we not tidy up the outhouse and make room for it there?" I suggested.

On inspection, this seemed quite impossible as there was hardly room to stand, but in Ireland the impossible has a habit of becoming fact, so that I achieved a satisfactory blank corner for the stout. As the outhouse faced the newly completed conveniences, Paddy coined a joke which kept him giggling all day.

"Sure 'tis the outhouse that's become the stout-house in front of the bout-house!" he crowed.

At last, "That's done," he said, rubbing his hands with the pleased and righteous expression of one who has supervised hard and successful work without lifting a finger. " 'Tis shipshape we are now!"

There followed a few days of resting on our oars as regards the pub. I didn't feel quite ready yet to tackle the major project of the cocktail bar, and therefore devoted the intervening time to making a closer acquaintance with some of my customers.

Their numbers were increasing steadily as they found the atmosphere novel, yet not breaking with the traditions they loved. It was important, I found, that I should serve as many as possible myself. The humbler the drinker, the more he preferred to be looked after by the owner rather than the barmaid.

This meant far longer hours and far more work for me than I had intended or anticipated, but by the same token it hastened my assimilation and my understanding of the people.

It also meant that as I was always there, there could be only a minimum of trouble with my assistants, whom I need not therefore regard with suspicion—an attitude that I can never adopt with comfort or conviction.

It was at this time that I met another female publican from whom I really learned the trade as it is practised in Cork. In passing I must say that one of the many unusual things that are profoundly pleasing about Cork seemed to me to be the complete absence of trade feuds. I never met a single body in the bar trade who didn't treat me kindly and as a friend, as it were a fellow club member, although we belonged to no set organizations.

It was, of course, through the ubiquitous Paddy that I met Daisy, who was to become a dear friend and a constant irritant to all my foreign prejudices, to fill me with admiration and with disgust, to baffle and enlighten me—and always to make me laugh.

"Ye've no one here yet, Mrs. O'," said Paddy one morning. "Leave the house to Bridie now, and come with me to meet Daisy. 'Tis a fine woman she is, and big-hearted!"

Consumed with curiosity about the new Mrs. in the district, poor Daisy had been unable to leave her business to come around and have a "small lookeen," for she couldn't afford a barmaid. Paddy, who was a diplomat of the first water, was not above accepting a small pot or two in exchange for information, nor had he been averse to the suggestion that I might be prevailed upon to visit her.

Not fifty yards away from Daunt's Square as the crow flies, and not more than three minutes' Irish walk, was a tumbledown building identical with its neighbours, bearing in faded gilt on its unwashed, but decorously curtained window, the simple legend "MURPHY'S STOUT."

This distinguished it from the pawnshops, the food stores, the houses with no outer indication of the obvious business pursued within, and those with small brass plates bearing high-flown business names, the full purport of which I was to learn later.

Paddy ushered me in with the musical-comedy old-world elegance which he did so well—and bewildered and blinded for a moment by the darkness, I stood still.

Only my nose recognized the place. It had the now familiar malt smell, unmistakable and no longer distressing, but here it carried a suggestion of misery, bearing as it did the addition of dust, cats and ancient cookery with an emphasis on cabbage. As I grew accustomed to the gloom, I saw on my immediate left, and in relief to the deeper darkness beyond, a door into what looked like the galley of a very small fishing-craft.

A longish table entirely filled the space between two benches: one with its back to the window surmounted by half-curtains of the dusty purple to be seen draping the church-bound saints during Lent; the other backed by a partition culminating in frosted glass—a discreet declaration of a privacy not to be disturbed, underlined by the word SNUG.

52

On the table were two small glasses and a half-empty pint of stout. A little hunchbacked woman, with a smile of extraordinary sweetness and pepper-and-salt hair, sat at the end of the table, facing me. On her right was a stout, ugly, mean-looking countryman, his nails long and black as he reached for his pot of beer, his eyes small and vicious, his belly straining absurdly at his fancy waistcoat. For a moment, I couldn't tear my eyes from the violet, maroon and apple-green diamonds that graced it—held back from outer space by the sheer moral effect of a watch-chain so imposing as to convince, despite all other appearances, of its mayoral quality.

I was drawn from this brief trance by a loud cheerful greeting from Daisy herself, heaving her short immensely stout body to a half-standing position, her bottom resting against the partition. "Come into the snug, girl; come in, Paddy Donovan!" she yelled. "What'll ye be after having, Mrs. O'? Yerrah, Paddy, don't stand there, boy, get Herself a drink—and I don't need to be telling ye to look after yerself?"

Summoned by the stubby crooked finger, I wriggled into the pew beside her, and tried to answer the spate of her questions about the pub.

"I hear 'tis terrible swell ye're making it," she said. " 'Tis all the talk."

Whilst we exchanged information about our mutual customers, and she extracted every detail of the redecorating we were doing, I had the opportunity of observing her without its being obvious.

Wildly overpermed and undercombed hair stood up in a black, vibrant, Medusa-like halo around a face which must have been fresh and pretty before the encroachment of fat and caries. She had twinkling green eyes set far apart, a very snub nose, a wide, well-shaped mouth in which a few

dark stumps stood well away from each other in mutual dis-
taste when she smiled. (I was often to hear her exclaim
later, "Wisha, 'tis good to come home from church," or
from wake, wedding or whatever social occasion had neces-
sitated the finding, dusting, insertion and wear of the hated
"set," which was removed even before her shoes when she
returned.)

She wore musty, rusty black from head to foot, and a
vast brooch, equally sombre and very ornate, which I felt
certain contained either a great deal of defunct hair or a huge
divot of soil from the Holy Land. It lay almost horizon-
tally on her vast breastworks, rising and subsiding rhyth-
mically so that had she wished to hypnotize me, I could not
have resisted.

Daisy lived her life thoroughly, enjoying all that it
brought, grieving with immense feeling and energy over
the larger and smaller tragedies which beset her constantly,
her philosophy unconscious and scatter-brained. She was the
complete extrovert, and in a crazy way one of the most balanced people that I have ever met—a cross between Bottom
and the Glaxo Baby.

At this first meeting I learned only some of the story
tangled around her by fate, like untidy knitting, not an
unusual story in Ireland, but to me at the time, new and
frightening.

Her husband, after two years in bed with tuberculosis,
had died a few months before our meeting (hence the weeds
which I should have thought much older). He had been a
heavy burden of expense and extra work. Her widow's sorrow was therefore pure and untainted. Genuinely sentimental and tempered by a little time, it had become one of
the most pleasurable subjects for conversation and gentle
day-dreaming in her existence.

Of course, the late-lamented Joe acquired—God save

him, and rest his soul—qualities and charms which each telling enhanced, so that when, a tear in each green eye and a suitably black handkerchief raised in readiness, Daisy fell to describing his demise, he was already a paragon of whom I felt secretly she was well rid—since no woman could ever survive such intolerable perfection in her mate.

"Ah 'twas the lovely man he was, Mrs. O'! And the best father in the whole world. When he couldn't get up anny more, I'd be telling the children to leave him be. 'Ah no, Daisy,' he'd say. 'Sure 'tis too lonely for them I'd be!' So he'd have the small ones in the bed with him and around him always. Jesus, Mary and Joseph, 'tis hard to be a widder with fatherless children!"

My flesh crawled at the gruesome notion of the dying man ensuring the death of his succession with the superb egoism of ignorance and sentimentality.

I made the appropriate inquiries about the children: the first and the third had died, as is quite customary, in infancy. The second was Eilie, aged sixteen, big, buxom, plain and terribly self-conscious, which I found so rare in Ireland that it surprised me. This child was useful to her mother in dealing with the younger children and the ordinary household responsibilities, which in any case did not appear to weigh very heavily with Daisy. But she stubbornly refused to have anything to do with the bar, for which I secretly applauded her.

She was the pious one of the family and had an old woman's passion for gossip and scandal which provided me with many an entertaining half-hour, for she took a liking to me and used to come to my pub quite often, where, curiously enough, she was always willing to pour a pint or serve a shawlie for me. I was careful not to thank her for her help, or to draw attention in any way to the difference in her attitude towards my customers and those who frequented her mother's bar. Perhaps she took pleasure in doing the identical work because it was neither a duty nor a necessity.

Daisy's second daughter was Ida, who had been her father's favourite and not inconsequently was now, at the age of twelve, in a sanatorium with galloping consumption.

I was prevailed upon without difficulty to drive the entire family to visit the young invalid when time and trade allowed. The first time we did this I accompanied them into the great hospital on one of Cork's lovelier hills.

What a place to recover in! I thought, surveying the well-groomed sleeping lawns, the perfectly kept flower-beds, the long airy verandas peopled with silent occupants of deck-chairs—reading, knitting, or gazing blankly at the distant glints of the Lee, furtive through the fields. White-robed nuns glided like swans amongst the backwaters of blooming, festering disease—as similar to riotous health as the rouge-pot to the peony.

Fear and revulsion swept over me as I saw my car-load enter a ward, approach one of the beds, and surround its occupant so closely that for a minute I couldn't see her.

They kissed her, hugged her, clung to her; they sat on the edge of the bed, sloping it with unconscious weight. The child was hugely excited. She began to cough. Her haemorrhages had set in already, and she had never been taught the polite concealment of a cough. My head swam and for a moment I could only see, as if through a microscope, the millions of joyous tubercular infectives launched freely at new defenceless blood.

How could they, I stormed inwardly, now—in the twentieth century—in the age of clinics, and antisepsis, and health campaigns! How could they?

Back in the car, horror and fury and disgust raging inside me, I forced a quiet tone as I asked about the child's condition. What did the Sisters say?

Daisy's tears were flowing freely onto the vast brooch and its purlieus. The nuns thought she had better bring the child's habit up next time—or at least have it ready. Ida was a member of some children's sodality whose members wore, on such occasions as processions or their own funerals, the habit of a certain religious order.

" 'Tis two haemorrhages she's had already," wept Daisy, "and there's no hope after three—and she, the lovely child —never a bit of trouble!"

I couldn't speak—out of a blend of pity and anger. Some days later I learnt that Eilie was cycling the ten miles out to the sanatorium and back to sit with her dying sister.

I tackled the child gently, telling her that I hoped that she was careful not to sit too close to Ida, pointing out the ease with which the disease is transmitted.

"Sure," said Eilie calmly, "if the Good God wants me to get it, then I will—and if He don't, I won't. Sure I couldn't sit away from me own sister, and her sick and all!"

This supreme religious fatalism, the utter disregard of the "free-will" clause, was to be my greatest stumbling block in Eire where disease and distress follow so inevitably in the wake of superstition, ignorance and dirt. Yes, and obstinacy too.

Only Daisy's greatness of heart and her tough resilience to poverty, hardship and misfortune, prevented my headlong flight from the horrors of each visit.

Godliness there was in plenty under her roof. Cleanliness came erratically to certain corners when circumstances dictated—which was rarely indeed.

In the depths of poor lighting; crowded, vulgar, grubby furniture; cats, and enamel basins full of grey suds and secret garments; unblown and unwiped noses, and glasses full of evil-smelling dregs, she and her brood subsisted precariously over her place of livelihood.

57

Their staple diet consisted of tea, bread and jam, and innumerable bags of greasy yellow chips from the man across the road. When there were guests (for Daisy loved a "party"), there was marble cake (in every sense of the word), and a nice fry—ugh! There were no bedtimes nor hours of rising, no mealtimes, no bath nights. There was always plenty of work, although she made a bare living from the pub. This was mainly due to her utter lack of business acumen combined with a generosity and an easy-going attitude towards credit which took my breath away. This wide-open, help-yourself lavishness of hers was completely instinctive—in no way prompted by moral or religious considerations. Indeed, it was amoral. To me at the time, full of the prejudices of another world, it was immoral. It seemed to me that in the manner of a blowsy Clytemnestra, she was sacrificing her own on the altar of some vague, general, sacred weakness. It was not at all uncommon for the entire family to go hungry for a day or two as a result of Daisy's helping some lame dog over a financial hurdle. My protests, inspired by genuine concern and affection, had no more effect than a child's logical conclusions on false premises may have on indulgent parents:

"Yerrah, girl," Daisy would smile, " 'tis not abroad ye are, nor 'over'!"

I couldn't help comparing her way of life with that of a remarkable woman I met around the same time.

She was in her fifties, round and red, and she conveyed an impression of sheer solidity. Her name was Kelly—although that is quite irrelevant—and she had been the only daughter of a wealthy butcher who, when his three sons were killed in the same action during the Revolution, had hanged himself the next day from an oak tree. Whether, in his sorrow, he had simply chosen the first tree that came to hand, or whether there had been some purpose in his choice, no one knew, but it happened that when the British Garrison

Commander's wife opened her bedroom window she looked straight into his glazed eyes as he revolved slowly on the rope.

Mrs. Kelly found herself the heiress to a prosperous business of which she knew nothing. She wrapped a blue and white apron around her middle, forgot the delicate embroidery the good nuns had taught her, and twenty years later she had the best butchery in the city—and three fingers left.

Her sons and daughters all had trades although they didn't need them, and her husband, behind a little glass cage, purred contentedly over the bloodied pay-chits. To me, each meat-hook dangling from her well-stocked racks symbolized the great initial of success.

Daisy provided the perfect contrast. It is a fact that my respect for Mrs. Kelly was immense, but it was Daisy who was my friend.

Although she had grown up in pubs, she belonged to a generation which was not encouraged to undertake men's jobs, and Daisy had never tapped a barrel. Learning of my success in this matter, she formed the opinion that I would repay teaching the secret arts of the trade, and it became quite common for her to come over and give me instruction at the slack times.

She joined Paddy Donovan's exclusive Committee on Advising Mrs. O', and one of her earlier contributions in this capacity proved to be of solid value.

6 ❖ Prayers and a Picnic

It was Saturday.

Daisy came over in the Holy Hour, dragging the thin, pale, whining, huge-headed Timmy in her wake. The child's lustreless eyes were enormous, his little face that of a frightened, whitened skeleton. He clung to her with the pitiful strength of a baby ape. He spoke seldom, in a voice pitched high on a peak of tears. Daisy sat down and he climbed into her lap, sprawling out in eternal weariness.

As I carried out the small tasks that permit of desultory conversation, she chattered, her shoes poised on the tips of her toes as her protesting feet relaxed.

"What Mass are ye going to, ever?" she eventually inquired.

Now my upbringing had consisted so largely of cold, numb knees on marble aisles—of halitosis through brass confessional grilles, of fish on Fridays, and accepting my crosses, and returning good for evil—that adolescence had brought surfeit, and maturity had done nothing to alter the feeling, so that for years I had made no effort to comply with the distasteful duties.

"I don't usually go at all," I told Daisy.

Her reaction was so unexpected that I roared with laughter.

"Yerrah, girl," she said, shocked to the core, "ye won't have a single customer in a month if ye're not seen going to Mass!"

It was a delicious piece of Cork philosophy—the inseparable relation of profit to faith, of hypocrisy to gullibility—sickening, shocking and vastly funny together. I was beginning to see that, despite the eccentricity of Irish ways as compared with those I knew, certain tenets of social existence were just as strictly observed in Eire as in a bourgeois suburb of Leeds or Lille. You have to swim with the tide, and if, faced with such an absurdity as confronted me then, you can only laugh or cry in impotent rage—well then, laugh and submit gracefully.

"I haven't got a hat," I protested feebly.

"What's wrong with a scarf, sure?" said Daisy calmly, and proceeded to point out that the "short twelve o'clock" would be best for me. She obligingly mentioned the existence of a convenient side door for easy exit "before the last prayers."

Encouragingly she added, "Sure, ye'll not be more than a quarter of an hour there, and everyone goes to the twelve o'clock—they'll all see ye!"

It became a routine, like visits to the brewery—an act of regular business necessity—its hypocrisy made tolerable by the huge joke of it all.

Shortly before noon the following day, I put on the newly purchased hat with great ceremony; gloved and armed with my old missal (a huge volume, impressive in its bulk and sombre binding), and informing Bridie in a clear carrying voice that I was "off to the Cathedral," left my customers nodding approval around the bar.

Memory of childhood things dies hard. At the back of the crowded church near the ornate pink font (not unlike the many baby bottoms that it had sanctified) I went through the drill quite unconsciously. The Latin responses sprang to my lips with the inevitability of breathing, and my senses responded as always to the odour of dead flowers, incense and sanctity, and the vibrations of liturgical music. Through the gauze of vagueness—my mind a thousand miles away—lilies, lighted candles and vestments of Biblical brilliance were no more arresting in their familiarity than the seascape is to the sailor. Only the charm of the ritual penetrated my consciousness—not as a vivid impression but as the atmosphere of a mood, meaningless in itself and purely sensual.

Someone knelt beside me at the end of the pew, and I moved a little to make room, still dreaming on.

"Et cum spiritu tuo . . ." and we all sat.

My glance fell on the hands beside me, sketching minutely on a small card the fervent profile of the old woman seated in front of me—a worthy subject. A shiver came over me as I recognized the broad fingers and the small black hairs on them. By an effort of will I didn't raise my eyes. The bell rang for the *Sanctus*. I knelt, my missal open before me on the narrow shelf, my knees, unused to the long-lost discipline, cracking loudly. I looked down from the distant altar to the pages of the Prayer Book, from which I saw protruding the corner of a card. I had long since got rid of the innumerable holy pictures that used to fall out of the book so embarrassingly often, and was therefore moved to turn the page and look. I think I knew before my hands moved that it would be the small sketch of the old woman. Under the drawing, in minute semi-Gothic script, I read: "Could you drive me into the country this afternoon? I have to see some people I think you will enjoy."

I looked at him briefly and nodded. In an inner flurry of reasoning I told myself that Sunday afternoon was the slackest time of the week. Bridie could cope. I needed some fresh air, the drive would do me good. I swerved around the knowledge that it would have hurt to have refused.

"*Ite Missa est. Deo Gratias.*"

The final wide sweeping sign of the Cross (Nanny telling me as if it were now, "Don't be half-hearted; genuflect *right* down to the ground, cross yourself *proudly*"), and out through the promised side door.

He preceded me and held the door open with the ordinary courtesy of a stranger to any woman. Outside, there were Sabbath crowds, scarfed like Russian refugees, coated and crudely gloved, bearing rosary and Prayer Book and chattering with the relief of birds let out of a cage.

He walked beside me and spoke as though we had been interrupted in a conversation.

"What time then?" he asked.

"I shall have to tell Bridie I shan't be in this afternoon. Shall we leave in about half an hour? I can get some sandwiches."

"No need," he said. "I've got a basket packed and a couple of bottles. Pick me up at the north end of the Coal Quay, will you?" and with a smile he was gone.

He had not envisaged a possible refusal, I thought. Yet I felt no annoyance. The ordinary conventions had not yet been observed between us. I didn't even know his name. It seemed to be of no importance. We might have been the first people on earth and it seemed natural to behave naturally. The exception became the rule and the experience and accumulated wisdom of the years seemed to count for nothing. I was as carefree as a seventeen-year-old making her first rendezvous.

With her usual stolid calm, Bridie accepted without question my decision to spend the afternoon in the country, but suggested that I wrap up warmly. City bred, she considered "de bogs" a shocking place for chills.

I slipped a bottle of Paddy and a couple of small glasses into the glove compartment and drove hurriedly to my flat.

A quick wash, and I donned warm boots (even in my

exhilaration I remembered the general inefficiency of my circulation), tore down the steps and started the car rather like an escaping criminal in one of the more hair-raising American movies.

He was standing by the water—the turbulent Lee, clear in the frame of the bogs, but here vitiated by the city's influence and dark and sinister. On a bollard beside him was a basket covered by a white napkin, startling in its purity against the sombre half-tones of the Coal Quay.

I drew up near him and opened the door. He put the basket on the rear seat and climbed in. I noticed his long legs seeking some comfortable position, adjusting themselves to my short driving reach.

I eased the small car through the crowds, changed up, and we were in the clear.

"Which way?" I asked.

"Roughly north," he replied.

"But aren't we going somewhere specific?"

"Yes, but there's no hurry. Take any way out of town you like—we can circle around afterwards—I know the country pretty well. . . ."

We took the west road, past the "Wimbledon" villas, the neat front gardens; out further past the new estates gazing in refined seclusion at the 'Sylum far across the river; out through the flats—green and lonely—the hills remote on either side, the river everywhere, its loops hopelessly entangled in pasturage and peat.

On through the woods, sad with an Irish sadness uncaused and unconsequential; over the bridges, through lanes dark in the sunless noon.

It was not cold: the day had been dropped by the wind into a soft grey suspense unrelieved by rain or sound.

"Are you alarmed at all?" he said then. "At yourself— or perhaps at me? Are you?"

Before replying I drew in by the side of the road, waited a moment to consider his curious question, and then said, "No."

It was true. I had ceased to analyse and to reason—at least for the time being. I followed the current as it swept without query or doubt. Some subconscious awareness that a condition was within my reach, deeper and more rewarding than ordinary existence had shown me, eliminated all superficial considerations and social anxieties.

How much of this pleasing frame of mind was due to the ubiquitous Celtic mystery and how much to the man beside me—and possibly how much to the long solitude that had gone before—I didn't know, and didn't care to know. He fitted perfectly into a half-mystical and half-physical receptiveness that had been building up since my plane touched down at Shannon.

"You needn't fear me—and please don't," he said, "for I couldn't hurt you. But if you're a little afraid of yourself, and I think you may be, it will not harm you to conquer that fear. You'll grow—traits that you don't even suspect you have will flower, and everything will suddenly become yours to cherish and to enjoy—if only you once decide to please yourself entirely—just once. Think about it—there's plenty of time."

He leaned forward and planted a swift, friendly kiss on my forehead. His lips were cool and half-smiling, but his eyes were very serious and their blue was darker than I had ever seen it.

"Drive a little further on," he said, before I had breath enough to speak. "There's a good place for a picnic just over the rise."

Like a puppet I obeyed, and stopping when he told me to, I saw that he had indeed chosen well. A small amphitheatre of rocks encircled grass cropped short by the sheep.

In this magic circle was a ring of large flat stones, white and smooth, astonishingly like the pediments of long-fallen temple columns, their marmorean calm undisturbed by the passage of time and the elements. The land sloped away from the road, which trees hid, towards a river running very swiftly and silently between silver-pebbled banks; beyond low-lying pasture spread lazily to the confines of a forest thrown over the hills like a dark hairy blanket.

He unpacked the basket, sitting on one of the flat stones.

I was in a mood where nothing seemed surprising, but my eyes widened at the sight of a bottle of a very good champagne, liver *pâté*, a cold chicken and other somehow incongruous delicacies. I saw none of the ham sandwiches or the Guinness I had expected. The unreal atmosphere of the day seemed to crystallize in the elegance of such fare in this wild remoteness: the brilliant foil of the champagne bottle winking with Gallic amusement at a huge Irish joke.

Suddenly he caught my eye and we both started to laugh—perhaps at the relaxation of the tension—or perhaps just as a child laughs—because we were happy.

He waved his hand in a grandiloquent gesture, twirled an imaginary moustache and "The scene is set!" he said pompously. "Champagne and a romantic landscape!"

I think excitement makes one particularly hungry. We ate almost in silence, greedily and with great pleasure. The pop of the cork echoed weirdly among the rocks and we started to laugh again. Life was very kind and had not brought its troubles to the party.

When we had packed up the remains of the meal and the smoke of our cigarettes was rising in parallel lines through the stillness of the day, he looked at his watch and asked me, "What would you like to do for the next hour or so?"

I wanted to say so much—but something held me back.

nd I replied, "Why? Are you in a hurry to get back to
Cork?"

I was afraid he would have some reason for curtailing
ours I wanted to be endless—but he laughed.

"I'm never in a hurry," he said. "I was wondering
whether you wanted to drive around, or explore, or sit still
—because we'll have tea at the Murphys' farm, and I know
their teas. I don't think we could do it justice until five or so."

"Let's just sit here, then. It isn't cold, and it's so
beautiful. . . ."

I leaned against one of the marble-like stones, replete
but not drowsy—half of me satisfied and contented, and
the other half alert and waiting, not with any urgency but
just enough for me to feel the pleasure of anticipation.

We talked of everything and of nothing—the world,
people, their funny doings, silly things and their deep metaphysical reasons. We might have been two old club members
meeting over a tattered copy of the *Tatler*, or fellow-
passengers on a Channel steamer, finding in congeniality sur-
cease from sea-sickness.

Both of us had gone beyond the impetuous years when
waiting of any kind is torture. Rather did we enjoy the quiet
suspense, like a wise child very slowly sucking a chocolate,
secure in the knowledge that the centre holds the cream,
and building up the anticipated pleasure through forbearance.

The time passed swiftly in idle conjectures about the
history of the fascinating white rocks, in jokes about the Coal
Quay folk, in his absorbing stories of the country which he
knew inside out—strange, sad stories some, and some up-
roariously funny. Of course, I enjoyed the ones about my
customers most.

I chuckled at his account of young Jimmy Shea's preparation for his First Holy Communion.

"You probably know Shea?" he said. "He comes into your place on market days. Big chap with a sort of gentleman farmer look: never buys anyone a drink. . . ."

I remembered the man. He kept his money in a small leather purse with a zip-fastener, and always groaned when he pulled it from his pocket.

"He has the best poultry farm in the county," he went on, "and the egg contracts for the hospital and the hotels.

"Well, his son, young Jim, had been learning his catechism and the priest was invited to tea one day shortly before the examinations.

"Mrs. Shea had everything polished up, roses in a bowl and the best lace cloth on the table. They talked for a while about parish matters. Father O'Connell tried to talk her into helping the church funds a bit more and she hedged neatly and after a bit he turned his attention to the boy.

" 'Now tell me, Jim, do ye know the holy days of obligation?'

" 'I do, Father,' replied the child, and reeled them off

" 'Fine, fine,' said the priest, lighting his pipe. 'Now tell me, boy, which of the holy days do ye think the most beautiful?'

" 'Easter Sunday.'

" 'Yes, yes,' nodded the good Father. 'And tell me, why is this lovely feast your favourite?'

"It was then that Mrs. Shea dropped the best teapot and ruined her lace tablecloth.

"Young Jim replied, ' 'Cause Easter Sunday I has an egg for me tea.' "

In one of the companionable silences that fell between us, he said, "You haven't been long in Ireland; how did it feel to you at first? Barbarous, wild, asleep, or just pretty pretty romantic? Do you think of it all as a highly coloured picture-postcard? Can you find anything real in it?"

"It's all real to me," I answered, "even the picture

postcard bits. There doesn't seem to be any dividing line here between fact and fancy, funny and tragic, good and bad. I'm too lazy to try and sort it out—anyway, I *like* it all jumbled up. One can't feel worthless or wicked or stupid here. Everything is only worth what it yields, and I'm taking greedily all the time."

"Good!" He said it warmly, emphatically, and repeated, "Good. How wonderfully un-Irish to *know* one is doing that!"

And I found myself telling him, with delight, of the small experiences I had enjoyed since my arrival; of the glamour in the wet lonely countryside which made me want to share the wakes, the tragedies and the poteen; to sit by pungent turf fires and listen to glorious chronicles devoted impartially to Brian Boru, Fontenoy, The Troubles, and what the "bhoys" did to them Germans—terrible hard cases they were—almost as bad as the English! And the splendid night when the ghosts joined us, invited rather grumpily by the two old men arthritized into curiously oak-like shapes, and I looked over my shoulder anxiously on the way up the rickety steps to my musty-smelling feather-bed, the flame of my candle flickering absurdly with my fear.

He laughed. "Didn't you say to yourself: 'Mad, all of them! Mad Irish'? Didn't you wonder how we managed to survive our own lunacy? We're just the same in all directions, you know. One day you must take a look at our political picture!"

Proudly I retorted, "I have!" and told him of my visit to Bantry.

There were several pubs in the little fishing port, the owners of which would gladly have retired on the profits of a sale to solvent, if insane, foreigners. None of them filled the bill, but the night I stayed at the least unprepossessing was a night for me to remember.

The elections for the Dail Eireann (the Irish Parlia-

ment) were coming up and that was the night "Dev" wa
to speak in Bantry Square. Much agitation and excitement
there were those who swore by Fianna Fail and those wh
spat on the floor at the mention of anything but Fine Gael
but all were sufficiently unspoiled as regards public enter
tainment to wish for a sight of the famous man who was the
Prime Minister—the "Taoiseach."

It rained with the usual Gulf Stream calm. The littl
town was soaked and the unwonted lights made everything
shine unbearably against the black pall of the sky.

The evening meal, adorned by ketchup and shared with
three commercial travellers in brown suitings, was followec
by a mass exodus to the lounge, where glass doors to th
street allowed at least two people to watch the proceedings

About nine, under a raised umbrella, a little man stoo
in the waterlogged square, looking old, cold and not ver
clever. He spoke, first in Gaelic—and the youngsters, un
daunted by the rain and the dignity of the occasion, recalled
their latest Irish lessons to mind and roared their support
Then he addressed the sodden crowd in English and th
older people knocked the dottle out of their pipes, pulled
their shawls more closely around them, and began to take
notice.

De Valera's sounded exactly like every electioneering
speech I have ever heard, and it was no surprise to me when
the Coalition Party, headed by Costello, swept into power
but even through the platitudes the curiously mystic quality
of the people shone like a beacon, reminding one of the
things of the heart and soul that are felt and unspoken. H
was boring and very thrilling, the little figure-head of ar
ancient struggle, at last successful and ended in the sluggish
ignominy of slipshod tourism. . . .

For a few moments he said nothing, and then, grinning
he placed a hand on my arm. "There's a story I think you'l

70

ike. It seems that hundreds of years after St. Patrick chased he snakes from Irish soil, he heard that the Irish were be-aving very badly. Making fools of themselves. From his eat among the clouds he stated gravely, 'We must suffer ools gladly.' 'But, St. Patrick, they're destroying themselves ntirely, attacking each other like snakes!' . . . 'Like nakes, eh!' St. Patrick sighed and took another puff at his ipe. 'Didn't I just tell ye we must suffer fools gladly?' "

I mused idly on the word "fools." It brought back the tory of a truly Biblical fool—one which I did not tell him, vhich had moved me in a mad, uncomfortable way.

My friend Deirdre had a maid who was "simple, God ave her" and who inexplicably became pregnant. Her em-loyer, a woman of self-indulgence in legitimate appetites nd self-restraint in those considered less legitimate, had the generosity and the sense of humour of her *concitoyens* with-ut the inquisitorial cruelty of chauvinism. Instead of feeling rritation towards a girl who had "let her down," she sought he background story when her condition became obvious.

You see, the creature was so ugly, so dull, so incredibly ndesirable in her brute usefulness, that it was hard to elieve the facts. She was returning from church where she ad been to confession (though what the poor creature found n her life of wet floor-cloths and stuffed-up sinks that could e considered worthy of the confessional, I don't know), vhen "all of a sudden-like, it happened."

Her mistress's queries produced little more than this. How it had happened, Norah hadn't the faintest idea. But he knew quite clearly that something *had* happened, and he remembered the circumstances with vivid simplicity.

"But Norah," my friend asked her, "who was it?"

"Faith, I don't know, Mam."

"Well, can you remember *when* it happened?"

"Yes, Mam—the bells was ringin' and ringin'—that's

when, and it so cold, Mam—so cold—with snow. Then he pulls me into the alley, and Mam, the bells was still ringin' but it wasn't cold any more—it was all lovely and warm like when I fixes the boiler. . . ."

"Well," said my friend, "there hasn't been that much snow and bell-ringing since the New Year, and not before that for quite twelve months—so I suppose—about September?"

Strangely enough, the idiot woman seemed in no way to connect the child with her experience—she showed no feeling for it at all, and it was clear that the warmth and the music of the bells bore no relation in her mind to the small, screaming, red creature they had produced.

The sequel was really my favourite part of the story. Deirdre, who loved food and fires and beauty and music, and who in her fat and chastity had never looked at a man, nor I think been looked at by one, became obsessed with the words of her half-wit servant.

The idea of such a chance unsentimental union in its unlikely frame of snow and chimes, the unexpected life-bringing warmth Norah had described, stayed in her imagination. She loved the child, adopted it, and is still delighted with it. Its mother tends it carefully and faithfully as she does her mistress's cat, and the mistress, I think, has almost forgotten that her bondmaid bore the child, remembering only the warmth in the snow and the joyous peal of bells she never heard.

I must have smiled at my thoughts, for he leaned forward and raised my chin with a cool finger.

"I won't offer you a penny for them. There's a twinkle in your eye, so I'll bid a shilling?"

Shaking my head, I refused, laughing.

"Ah, 'tis the cruel colleen ye are," he scolded, "and me after *dying* with curiosity!"

"*You* are!" I exclaimed. "What about *me?*"

Instantly the teasing grin left his face and the sombre, excluding look returned. He got up and walked away in silence and I could have bitten my tongue out.

A few moments later he came back with a minute bunch of daisies, which he handed me solemnly.

"I'm a bad-tempered bastard," he said, sitting down beside me. "And you're very lovely and very kind to me—and very forgiving, aren't you?" and he put his arms around me and held me close for a moment. Like a child, he kissed my cheek and then pulled me to my feet.

"Let's go over the hill now—to the Murphys' . . ." with his most angelic smile.

I followed him, as I would have followed him anywhere.

7 ⁚ Tea with the Murphys

Over the hill the country became more open and the fields showed more varieties of green, promising splendid bargaining on the Coal Quay. The land looked good, and it seemed the Murphys must be among Cork's more prosperous farmers: the dykes were in good repair, the cattle coming in to be milked looked sleek and well fed, the crops spoke of good manure and husbandry.

The farmhouse, partly hidden from us by tall trees, was nearly as well built as the barns. This in itself bespoke ease, for as every farmer knows, barns matter immensely; houses are of secondary importance, almost luxuries as one might say.

As we drove into the lane, a girl came running past drawn on by two impatient greyhounds. Her hair was flying and she pulled helplessly on the leashes. She was tall, very thin, and truly "foxy"—her mane was of that unmistakably Irish redness, her eyebrows and eyelashes sandy, but the dun-coloured freckles that so often disfigure this particular complexion were absent. Instead a superb white skin showed up the hectic colour of her cheeks. I had been in Cork long enough to recognize tuberculosis when I saw it—and yet, as I manoeuvred the car into the farmyard, I wondered.

"That's Sheila, the second daughter," he said as we got out.

Surely, I thought, surely a farm-bred child of prosperous people should be free from this plague of Ireland?

In the rush of introductions and welcomes, I forgot about it. The family were absorbing in themselves, and the strangeness of the atmosphere fascinated me, for it was my first visit to a Cork farm.

I sat on a stiff chaise-longue covered in stiff leatherette as smooth as polished glass, yet completely pervious to the stiff horsehair that kept me wriggling surreptitiously. Once again I was savouring the weirdness, the splendid mixture of beauty and squalor, of hum-drum and fairy-tale, the constant piling up of vivid contrasts that I was growing to crave like a drug.

Tom Murphy had inherited from his father a fine farm, two derelict elderly uncles, and an old-maid sister, who was clearly the ruling power in the house.

She was very small, grey and neat—and quite toothless. Her welcoming grin was startling in its baby-like blankness, the more ludicrous for the strong aquiline nose above it and the shrewd, piercing blue eyes. It was she who managed somehow, though taking part in all the conversation, to impart to me quite a substantial family history, whilst missing absolutely nothing that went on.

Her brother Tom, well off at an age when most young Irishmen can hardly keep themselves, had done what is unusual for that very reason: fallen in love and married a city girl, bringing her back in triumph to live there at Ballyfegan.

" 'Twas the pretty creature she was," said Kathleen, "but terrible delicate—no good for the worruk at all, at all."

This pretty creature had borne Tom a son who died at birth, and two daughters, one of whom I had already seen

75

outside. The elder girl came in a little later—Annie, a fine strapping mare of a creature, utterly unlike her sister.

No one had been surprised when the mother succumbed to phthisis shortly after Sheila's birth.

"Wisha, Tom's heart was broken entirely," Kathleen went on, "but the child was so like the mother that he took comfort in her, God save him."

Sheila had always been frail, and only now that she was eighteen was Tom beginning to feel easy in his mind about his darling. For they saw her lovely colour and her febrile energy and—God help them—they rejoiced.

This all came out in short sections—rather like a serial story—for there was immense bustle and activity, inspired by our presence and the consequent need to show hospitality.

We managed to persuade the clan that we preferred to join them in the kitchen, where they spent their leisure, rather than sit in gloomy state in the parlour—a sombre chamber redolent of the visits of parish priests, the reading of wills, and the surreptitious but olfactory presence of mice.

The kitchen had no refinements of the "immortelles under glass" variety—no closely vased bulrushes, no maroon repp at all and no antimacassars. The windows were spared the horrors of écru net and velvet *portières*, and there were no holy pictures on the walls.

The fireplace sported a great spit from which hung a hissing kettle. Settles lent their uncompromising rigidity to the accustomed comfort of long-standing bodies. In fact, everything in sight was purely useful, and as the thought of ornament had not occurred, so neither had the sin of bad taste. Everything was beautiful in that it served a purpose; everything was clean without fanaticism, that is to say, where it mattered. The table was snowy and scrubbed to ivory smoothness; the floors were muddied in cheerful acceptance of farm life. Cats and chickens moved around calmly, finding interesting crumbs under the furniture, and showing no apprehension until the dogs came in.

Oil lamps hung in odd places or, set down uncompromisingly on the table, provided a gentle yellow light.

Heavy farm boots stood drying near the fire, and from the mantelpiece hung woollen socks, steaming gently. The whole atmosphere was relaxed and cheerful, unstrained even by the energetic Aunt Kathleen, who was determined to provide a tea to end all teas.

Tom Murphy leaned back in the arm-chair by the fire—obviously the master's chair as there were no others—and surveyed the scene around him with visible satisfaction.

He was a large, solid man, still quite young, but running to flesh; his features undistinguished, but his bearing one of quiet unconscious dignity. He conveyed the feeling of restfulness and freedom from stress that countrymen living in close communion with Nature take for granted—but which is so rare in city folk.

His problems were all material ones and none of them tricky enough to disturb his soul. He talked very little, but listened with great attention to everything that was said, and his eyes went from one person in the room to the other, with expressions that changed for each, as the image in the water changes with the ripple of a breeze.

The old uncles, sitting either side of the fireplace like a couple of crouched book-ends, tired after a day of gentle pottering in an illusion of work, drew from him a gentle, tolerant smile—the smile of a man who can afford to be generous and enjoys his patriarchal responsibilities.

For Kathleen, he had the fond, exasperated and amused expression of the henpecked husband who appreciates his wife's worth.

For his visitors, a glance of increased brightness—a blend of curiosity and kindness, an appreciation of the unfamiliar. He was obviously fond of my companion and enjoyed the occasional visits he paid them.

Annie came in, her boots muddy, her hair pinned up roughly, her apron tucked high. She had been feeding the turkeys she raised for pin-money and loved so passionately that each sale was anguish, and she carried the huge empty basin which had contained their mash. With her came the fresh smell of farmyard: manure, straw, fodder. She grinned cheerfully, threw the basin down in a corner, and sat down on one of the settles near her father. He slapped her rump playfully as she passed, and there followed a short exchange of farm talk between them.

It was obvious that Annie adored the farm and that her father saw in her the son who assisted him and would succeed him in working it. But when Sheila came in, bright-eyed and smiling, his eyes lit up and his look of adoration followed her around the room. She moved nervously, helping her aunt a little, picking things up and then putting them down. She was gay and laughed at everything, but her hands were never still for a moment. Could she have known or suspected what none of the others did? There was a feverish quality to her vivacity, an uncertain brittleness which my stranger's eye, unblurred by familiarity or love, caught readily.

We talked of new fields being ploughed, of which Tom had great hopes, of the endless permutations of marriages, births and deaths in the county; and there was much delighted chatter about Tom's young nephew Jerry, who was going to Maynooth.

" 'Tis a great pride for the family," declared Kathleen. "And him so young. I always knew Jer would be a priest, sure, as I told him when he was that high. Yerrah, the Donovans will be after raging!"

This last with immense satisfaction. Obviously the Donovans, whom she disliked, were about to be confounded entirely.

I happened to glance at the man beside me and saw his whole body tense and a sudden look of acute discomfort, almost of pain, come to his face. His easy languid pose, one long leg crossed over the other, arms folded loosely on his breast, changed without movement to one of fear and tension. No one noticed.

The talk flowed on, and Kathleen began to serve the tea—a composite of many meals. There were the ham and eggs of the Anglo-Saxon breakfast—but what ham, and what eggs; the scones, sandwiches and bread-and-butter of the surburban tea-party; cakes of a birthday perfection; hot, coarse farm bread melting the butter before it could spread; and gallons and gallons of tea, strong, black, flowing endlessly.

Attempts to stick to single helpings were foiled quite firmly from the start, and we ate with a pleasure that soon became an effort. I looked at him again, and saw that he had taken a grip on himself. He was complimenting Kathleen on her light hand with pastry, and she was preening delightedly.

I wondered what could have caused him to look so distressed, but knew I couldn't ask him. The taboo on questions between us was unbreakable and, unless he chose to confide in me, would remain unbroken.

After the enormous meal had been cleared away, and the girls were busy in the scullery washing up, small glasses of the "company wine" were handed round—sweet and sticky. Kathleen glanced rather sharply at my cigarette, but only handed me an ash-tray, rather pointedly. It was a large bronze Infant Samuel at Prayer with a small dimple in the base which was apparently intended to hold pins. As the floor wouldn't have suffered from a hundred cigarette-butts, this was obviously a gesture, but one learns to take no offence in Ireland, and the balance of cordiality remains unchanged.

The family albums were brought out, and Sheila's embroidery and Annie's account books offered for inspection. And, of course, suitable praise. A family scene, warm and pleasant in its innocent pride and contentment. I wished I could not see the blight that hung over it and made me shudder inwardly with pity and revulsion.

We left late, accompanied to the car by the two girls and their father, bidding us return soon and sending all sorts of inconsequential messages to mutual friends in the city. The last I saw of Sheila was her brilliant hair caught in the beam of my headlights as I swung the car around into the dark road. I went there only once again—months later.

I drove slowly back to Cork, my mind full of the day's events, my body comfortably drowsy from the warmth and the heavy meal.

Beside me he sat silent until the glow of the city shone in the sky over the last low range of hills before the flats. It was very dark and the brightness of the headlights changed the soft outlines of bushes and bridges to brief flashes of form etched sharply against the blackness. The engine drummed gently and steadily like rain on the roof.

I wanted to look at him—I felt I could see him in the dim green light from the dashboard—but dared not take my eyes off the winding road.

At last, he sighed and said, "I shan't be seeing you again for a while. There are some rather trying things I must attend to. When I return, I'll take you to another farm one day. A lot of things will be clearer to you then. And listen, don't puzzle and worry. Keep on trying to understand through your heart, not your head. Go on collecting feelings and sights. Keep growing."

As we entered the town, he put his hand on my arm

and added gently, "Thank you for being discreet, macushla—anyway, why know anything except what one wants to?"

He asked to be dropped at the same place where I had picked him up on the Coal Quay, and when I stopped the car he held me very close for a moment, and kissed me. . . . All the emptiness and longing in both of us met in that moment.

Then he opened the car door, reached for the basket on the back seat, and in one movement disappeared into the shadows silently—and I sat watching the distant lights reflected in the surface of the grumbling Lee, but seeing nothing and feeling only a thousand nerves twitching all over me.

After some time, I sighed and drove back to the pub, where the Garda were just arriving for their nightcaps. They hailed me with pleasure, for Bridie was not as lavish with the free pots as I, and we went in together. They were full of gossip and the latest scandal that night, but my head started to ache unbearably, so I saw them comfortably provided with drink, greeted my customers, who were pretending to be travellers, and excusing myself on the grounds of fatigue, I left Bridie to lock up, and went home. Under the door when I opened it, I found a note addressed to me in the same tiny Gothic script. "Please be patient with me—you know I shall hurry back to you. Sean."

8 ❖ Inferior Decoration

"Top of the morning to ye, Mrs. O'!" said Pàddy Donovan in the tones of the stage Irishman—remote as Hottentot from the brogue of Cork.

"Have ye decided yet what ye want in th'upstairs room?"

It was a direct approach on the subject of the cocktail bar, my plans for which I had outlined to him briefly. I felt a trifle guilty about it, for I had done nothing at all since the idea first occurred to me, so I willingly took him upstairs to the large front room.

· The walls were papered in maroon, faded to an uneven brown in leprous patches. The woodwork, of course, was also brown, but an alcove with a rather lovely arch over it at the back of the room was painted a vivid pink. In the middle of this sea of colour, a square area stood out darker than the rest.

"Yerrah, there was a beautiful St. Joseph there," Paddy told me. " 'Twas a grand corner for a little altar, eh, Mrs. O'?"

I nodded silently.

"But sure, 'twould be even *better* for a bar," he assured me, "wid yerself standing under the arch, an' the counter in front like."

His critical eye dwelt briefly on the shape of the arch, and inspiration came.

"Coloured lights all round the top," he said, "an' tube lighting for the bottles. Sure 'twill be the *only* pub in Cork with inferior decoration!"

I was plunged into contemplation of myself framed by coloured lights on a background of floodlit bottles when we were interrupted by Sergeant Rooney of the Garda Siochana.

I asked him playfully whether he had brought me a summons, secure in the knowledge that the Guards were on my side. He expressed horror at the idea, and assured me that nothing so unpleasant would spoil my morning.

"No," he said, "I was just passing by like, and I remembered ye gave Phelan a helping hand a while ago, so I thought I'd drop in and tell ye the latest."

"What's happened to him now, Sergeant Rooney?" I asked. "Oh, dear—I do hope it isn't one of the children?"

"Ah, no—sure, Mam, this time 'tis just the usual. I told him a hundred times MacNamara's was too big a job fer him—and at first he took me advice—but now the foolish feller's gone and fallen for it. He's in his usual cell, Mam —and this time the bail's something wicked!"

He cocked a speculative eye at me, but said no more.

Paddy shook his head and sighed. I shook my head and sighed. The policeman shook his head and sighed even more deeply.

"It really is too bad," I said. "This time he deserves it."

I went downstairs, followed by the two men.

Sergeant Rooney stood beside me as I rummaged through the cash box, counting notes. When the amount on the counter was sufficient, he nodded and grinned.

"And him not worth sixpence! Will ye be coming to the court-house wid me, Mrs. O'?"

We went off together.

Rooney was a real gentleman, and had sought my help without letting Phelan know. When the cell door was opened and the little burglar saw us standing there, his face was a study in amazement and pleasure.

"Phelan, you terrible hard case!" I expostulated frowningly. "Aren't you ashamed of getting yerself caught again? For heaven's sake, man, don't do it again."

He saw the laughter I was trying to hide, and responded gaily.

"Yerrah, Mam, 'tis no chance I'll be having for a year or so. I'm after asking them for the key of the door, but they say I'll have to wait till I'm twenty-one!"

He was quite genuinely astonished to find he was free, and the laughter faded from his face. He wiped his nose with the ragged handkerchief that always protruded from his sleeve, and said in a low earnest voice:

"God bless ye, Mrs. O'. I'm ashamed and sorry, but ye know I don't *want* to do it. There's just nothing else. I owe ye enough, God knows, but if ye could only talk to someone, maybe at the brewery, I'd do anything for a straight job of work. . . ."

I promised to try—although I knew jobs were desperately scarce—and he hurried home full of hope, refusing to come back with us and celebrate his release.

We drank his health in a leisurely manner, Sergeant Rooney improving the shining hour by industriously rubbing out the notes in his notebook and altering them to read more or less incriminatingly according to his opinion of the culprits.

But Paddy Donovan was in a fever of planning, his fertile imagination weighing the rival merits of brass and timber bar-rails, terrazzo-topped tables, or chromium-plate. He had quite forgotten that the cocktail bar wasn't his own idea and his own property, and it was with a note of impatience in his voice that he said, "After we've had the one for the road, Mrs. O'" (which I hadn't suggested), "we'd better be going back upstairs and getting on with the job."

I told him that it seemed to me the first thing to decide was who was going to do the job. After all, he was an electrician, not a builder, or painter or plumber.

This timid nonsense he waved away as unworthy of attention. "The first thing, Mrs. O', is to choose the colours and the furniture—to go with the lights, of course."

I felt it was time to kill the idea of the coloured lights, and the look of pain on his face was pathetic.

"Ye just want plain, yellery white ones, like everybody else has? Just *ordinary* lights?" he protested incredulously.

I was firm. He shook his head dismally and departed in silence shortly after.

However, Paddy had the bounce of a rubber ball, and he was back within half an hour with his arms full of catalogues, brochures, samples of wall-paper and innumerable swatches of curtain material.

I threw up my hands in horror. For a moment it seemed that there was a conspiracy afoot to burgle the entire shopping centre in order that I should bail everyone out. Before I had time to say anything, though, he had spread his loot all over the counter and was rhapsodizing over it.

"I know ladies can't be after making up their minds unless they can handle the things, Mrs. O', so I got ye a few to choose from."

He handed me a gruesome piece of mauve material, patterned with scarlet dice.

"I thought that'd be one of the likely ones for yer curtains," he crooned.

As I went through the ghastly collection and listened to his enthusiastic commendation of the samples he fancied particularly, the words "inferior decoration" kept passing through my mind like some insane litany. When I chose the only one I liked—a charming French-grey with a thin, pale yellow stripe—Paddy was disgusted. "There's no life in it at all, Mrs. O'," he protested. "Yerrah, they won't even *notice* it!"

He brightened up a little when we turned to the paints, only to be cast down again when I selected a glossy black.

" 'Tis a *wake* they'll think it . . ." he said desperately.

"Never mind, Paddy—it won't show finger-marks, and it'll allow you to play with more lighting effects."

Paddy had really excelled himself with the wall-papers.

We stood surrounded by squares of pure lunacy—pink with chocolate roses a foot in diameter, beige with purple urns containing gamboge bulrushes, orange polka dots on a baby blue ground, and masses and masses of unlikely flowers on "cream." Ruthlessly I waded through these nightmares until Paddy was bowed like an old man. There were a few pieces of a pebbly neutral paper, and I looked at these, albeit briefly, but he saw a ray of hope.

"If 'tis something *plain* ye're wanting, there's some lovely dadoes. I brought a few."

I had never seen a "lovely dado" and was filled with curiosity.

Paddy unfurled a smallish roll, and I stood in stunned silence. Long strips of paper about a foot wide bore brilliant floral patterns, picked out with gold and silver gilt paint, and the borders were tortured into fantastic fringes and serrations like a child's untidy haircut. These apparently were guaranteed to "liven up" a plain pebbly wall and Paddy, I could see, thought them tasteful and gay. I was saved from having to comment on the dadoes by the sight of a promising corner under a huge pile of pink roses and green chrysanthemums. I pulled it out of the pile, and Paddy groaned. It was pale yellow with a small white fleur-de-lis pattern.

Chairs, tables and linos were less heart-breaking to Paddy, for there was little choice, and apart from his failure to install any terrazzo at all, he seemed quite contented when, at the end of a couple of weeks, the cocktail bar had everything except a bar. I couldn't make up my mind what sort of counter to put in. It had to be small, and I wanted it to look interesting.

One day Deirdre, who had a passion for "picking things up," persuaded me to attend an auction with her. I went in the spirit of an amused spectator.

In the huge bare hall a row of settles bore as varied a cross-section of Cork as one could wish for—shawlies, farmers, middle-class housewives, mothers with small snivelling children, tradesmen, tarts and corner-boys—they were all there. Deirdre and I arrived when the bidding had already started and we sat down on the end bench, she full of the buyer's zeal and I prepared to enjoy myself at no expense.

This particular sale had attracted a lot of attention because the goods were the legacy of a much-travelled and eccentric old man to heirs who liked Ideal Home chromium fittings and *petit-point* firescreens and couldn't live with his weird collection under their roof for another minute.

As we came in, the auctioneer, a large red-faced man with the gift of the gab carried to the ultimate peak of perfection, was playing on his audience like a violin.

He held aloft two copper warming-pans, a china chamber-pot of unusual charm (adorned as it was with a willow-pattern design), and a feather duster.

"Ladies and gentlemen! Here's four lovely useful things. Ye've a chance of gettin' four lovely things for the price of wan lot—just wan lot! Yerrah, dese pans—fer a nice fry there's nothing like copper—makes the bacon taste like pork steak! And ye wouldn't be after wanting to feel ashamed when 'tis visitors ye have—and yer house all dusty —sure a feather duster gets rid of the muck quicker 'n anything else. An' this," he said, solemnly brandishing the willow pattern, "this is terrible swell. Sure 'tis only fer guests ye'd keep it, and them impressed wid the good taste of ye. . . ."

The bidding started, rising jerkily under the impetus of his impassioned exhortations, and the lot was finally knocked down to a mean-faced woman in country clothes who was obviously actuated by a sense of snobbery so great that it mastered her avarice. Clearly she couldn't wait until her next visitor was assailed by the call of nature.

Lot succeeded lot, some worthless but fetching quite respectable prices, others containing really lovely things that appealed to no one. No one, that is, except Deirdre, who worshipped beauty and was squirming with excitement like a child at a party.

"Here," said the auctioneer, "is lot nine. One firescreen of the best brass wid a pitcher of"—he paused, inspecting the object carefully—"one brass firescreen wid a lovely pitcher on it." He went on, "Two hearthrugs, good as new except one has a small holeen burnt in it, but sure 'twouldn't show under a chair—like—and one small statcher."

Deirdre was fidgeting so much that I nudged her. She took the hint and waited until a half-hearted bid of half a crown had been made, and bettered by four shillings. Then she cocked an eyebrow at the auctioneer in the experienced way of the regular auction-goer. I have never been able to fathom how an auctioneer knows whether a wink means ten shillings or a nod six, but they do.

"Seven shillings I'm bid for this grand artistic lot—

seven shillings *only*. Aren't ye all ashamed of yerselves—wid nothing artistic in yer homes—jest ordinary *useful* things?" he exclaimed.

It is human nature not to want anything very badly unless someone else wants it too—which is why auctioneers pay a great deal of income tax. No sooner did Deirdre start to bid than two others did, too, and the bidding grew fast and furious, rising by sixpences after a while until the hammer came down in my friend's favour. She got the little statuette she had coveted valued some time later—and her instinct was proved sound. It was a genuine Chinese piece of a very good period and worth a great deal. Together with the firescreen and the rugs she had paid fourteen shillings for it.

Crimson with joy, she wanted to go, but I was enjoying myself and insisted that we remain a few minutes longer.

"Lot fourteen! Yerrah, here's a real elegant bit of furniture—an' handy, too. Sure they don't make them like this anny more. Look at them fat doors—and a drawer in the top too!"

It was a very small black sideboard, curved at the ends and painted down the front with the loveliest old-gold chinoiseries. Either side of the front panel were small cupboards with curved glass doors through which showed pale yellow satin gathered into innumerable tiny pleats on the little triangular shelves.

Two sweating men turned the lovely thing around so that the cupboards and drawers at the back showed clearly that it was useful as well as ornamental.

A fat woman in mauve with orange lipstick bid ten shillings.

The auctioneer's scorn was crushing. He appealed to our sense of the fitness of things, to our intelligence, to everything.

A voice called out from the back, "'Tis too small to be any good for anything, and too big fer house-room!"

This was greeted with guffaws, and even the auctioneer seemed surprised when I piped up with, "Fifteen shillings." People's sporting instincts were aroused at once and several who would have been absolutely dismayed to be landed with the thing bid against me, but cautiously, a shilling at a time. But the twenty-five shillings became too great a risk to take, and I had my counter for the cocktail bar.

Paddy frowned at it when it was hoisted up the narrow stairs. "An' how many pints can ye serve on that?" he asked disparagingly.

I pointed out that pints were not going to be a feature of the "upstairs trade" and, a little tersely, told him to mind his own business. He sulked tremendously for two and a half minutes until I asked him whether he could fit tiny lights inside the glass cupboards, hidden by the door-frames. His joy was indescribable, and the hated counter became his pet project. Indeed, with the soft lights shining on the faded satin and some very small miniature bottles on the tiny shelves, it looked charming and was a subject of conversation, even in other pubs, for months afterwards.

With a sigh of relief, I paid the bills (which were really not as bad as I had expected), and made a pilgrimage to the shrine of respectability on the top floor.

Mrs. O'Rourke was knitting, but courteously waved me to a chair. I explained that I needed a nice, well-brought-up girl for the new bar.

She was hesitant about letting either of her pretty daughters take the job on. "'Tis not that I think 'tis a low place, or anything like that," she assured me, "but 'twould be putting terrible temptation in a young girl's path."

I wasn't clear what kind of temptations my new bar could provide that were not equally accessible anywhere else. Surely she didn't think that the girls would "take to the drink" as a result of serving it?

She dismissed this as nonsense. It was the possibility that one of her daughters might get into the toils of some dashing frequenter of cocktail bars that worried her. Promising that I would naturally look after the girl if she worked for me, but adding that I didn't want to press her at all, at all, I rose to go. Hastily Mrs. O'Rourke said she would let Doris "try it for a small whileen," and we parted with expressions of mutual esteem and reassurance.

We fixed the opening date for the cocktail bar a week from the day the work was finished, and I ordered extra supplies of the appropriate drinks and started to teach the pretty and fluffy-headed Doris how to make "short ones."

Her eyes glued on the small book of cocktail recipes, a frown wrinkling her well-plucked brows, she would whisper, "Whoite Lady—gin, lime, frosting of sugar. . . . Martini, one part Vermooth, two of gin . . ." and so on.

Paddy Donovan offered his co-operation in this training scheme and soon he was an authority on Side-cars, Angel's Kisses and Rum Collins. Each time Doris mixed a drink, it was necessary to taste it and pronounce judgment.

Paddy's boasts to the outside world became unbearable. "Ah, 'tis a foine Manhattan the gerrul mixes now," he would say. "Just the right *touch* of bitthers!"

I couldn't quite share his undivided optimism, for I felt sure that Doris would get stage-fright and serve a gin-and-whisky with castor sugar on the opening night.

" 'Tis educating them we'll be," Paddy went on. "There'll be no one content wid a pint after this."

Here again we did not quite see eye to eye. I hoped the demand for pints would continue in the downstairs bar, as that was the real steady business, but by now Paddy was too grand for stout.

In common with other so-called "lounges" in Cork, I decided to sell only bottled beer upstairs, therefore we had to step up production in the period before the opening. Daisy, who was enchanted with the whole scheme, came over to help.

Every night, after closing, the following operation was carried out: the drip pans under the spigots were emptied into large jugs, then scoured, rinsed and left draining upside down all night. The contents of the jugs were then poured into the spiled casks of stout—but only the flat ones. This served the dual purpose of obviating any waste, and of accelerating the fermentation of the flat stout by the addition of the stuff which had been exposed to the air. This was a valuable speed-up to the process of obtaining high stout without having to hurry over using it. The high stuff delivered from the brewery only stayed in that desirable condition for a very short space of time. As the operation was a daily one and everything kept very clean, there was nothing wrong with the routine from a hygienic viewpoint, but as most people suspected in Cork that publicans used the dregs from glasses, it was something one couldn't do openly. As a matter of fact, I knew quite well that some publicans did do this—but I didn't. My bottled stout had a good name because I never mixed the brands, and was adamant about the proper cleaning of bottles and equipment—although, of course, the customers couldn't know this.

It was Daisy who taught me bottling, and this time when there was so much to do, she set to with a will.

As each cask of stout was topped up, we replaced the top bungs and smeared a little dust over them. From these we filled the bottles—Daisy pedalling away at the Crown corker, and I, rather better constructed for bending over, filling from the cask.

When we were satisfied that we had three weeks' stock

in reserve, allowing for the extra consumption that we hoped would result from the opening of the new bar, we tidied up, and stretched our weary backs. All was shipshape. The opening was tomorrow. We looked at each other with satisfaction and affection.

"Ye know, 'tis jealous of ye I'd be," she said, "if I didn't hold ye near me heart. 'Tis a grand business ye've got, and making it better all the time. I'll tell ye the truth, I'd not have thought ye could have run a pub in Cork with yer foreign ways and your long hair and all. People don't have anny respect for women that looks like girls. But it's a good business, and yer own making. Come over now, and have a cup of tea before ye go home."

I felt quite all-overish at this unexpected and indeed startling accolade. My eyes prickled and I mumbled, "I'd love to." This was such a lie that I felt it to be a small move in the right direction—for it was then midnight, I was bone-weary, and I knew Daisy's cups of tea: the endless time they took to be made, and the endless heartburn they provoked.

I didn't bother to take the car down the narrow streets to Daisy's, but left it in the parking space in the square, which by now—as though I had a season ticket for it—no one would have dreamed of occupying.

Daisy's children, of course, were still up. Timmy, who had spent most of the evening under the counter, sleeping in an empty soda-water crate, was now hungry and chips were bought from the never-closing man across the road.

Eilie had some new terrifying gossip for me which she could hardly hold until I sat down.

"Ye know that posh nursing home?" she began. "Well, the nursery for the new babies is in de basement-like, and a terrible thing happened yesterday, Mrs. O'. De nurses was having tea in the kitchen, and they heard the babies yelling something dreadful, and 'tis hungry they thought they were

—but 'twas a good half-hour yet to feeding-time, and they didn't go to look. And then wan girl couldn't stand it, and she went, and she found two big rats sitting in a cot and the baby's head half-eaten away, and it screaming still. It died though, while she looked. Oh Lord, everyone's terrible shocked, for such a thing's never happened in Cork at all!"

I was genuinely horrified, and resisted the impulse to say that if it were going to happen anywhere, I should have put my money on Cork as a likely place.

I drank the poisonous tea, washed it down with some Paddy which I hoped might counteract the evil effects, and took my departure at nearly two o'clock, completely worn out. I knew a tough day lay ahead and was mildly resentful about the loss of sleep, but I was so fond of Daisy and so grateful for her undemanding friendship that I bade her an affectionate good night and dragged myself off wearily.

The car, which I never locked, started with its usual calm, and I drove home at once, longing for bed. It was only when I lit the roof-light before getting out, to see if I had forgotten anything, that I saw a small envelope of the kind used for visiting cards, clipped with a paper-clip to my rearview mirror. I knew before looking what it contained. I ran up to the flat, closed the door behind me, and tore the envelope open with trembling fingers. The same tiny decorative writing, the superscription simply "Mrs. O'." Inside on a blank visiting card, "Tomorrow. Are you glad I'm back? Sean."

Like a schoolgirl I pirouetted in the narrow hall until annoyance struck me. What time? Where? How long to wait? He might have said . . . but it was only a token annoyance and I went to bed full of contentment.

9 ❧ The Launching of the "Lounge"

By a tradition of the trade, any new venture is launched on a Saturday night if this is at all possible. Therefore, when customers asked, "When is de new lounge starting, Mrs. O'?" it was sufficient to say, "Week after next" or "Next week." I had no need to advertise—the grapevine covered all advance publicity—and people who had never been upstairs were apt to ask me before the opening, why I had chosen yellow and black, or why lino instead of polished floors. For the meticulous accuracy of the information circulated, I knew I could thank Paddy Donovan and Daisy. They were far more excited than I was, and Daisy had gone to the lengths of closing her own pub for my opening night.

She was on my doorstep at five—two hours before I planned to christen my new bar—resplendent in skin-tight black velvet (rather rubbed at the tightest places) and dripping with jet jewellery. I was touched to see that she had cut her nails to the quick, and scrubbed her hands raw. The normally wild thatch of black hair had been tortured into tight ringlets, and she even wore the detested "set." This was too much. There are limits even to friendship.

"Take them out, Daisy!" I implored her. "I want you to enjoy yourself, too!"

With a huge sigh of relief, she whipped them out, wrapped them in a miraculously clean handkerchief, and put them in her bag.

"Sure, I was afraid ye'd be ashamed of me," she grinned.

Together we walked from the flat to the pub, Daisy holding herself terribly straight and trying to look unconcerned.

Bridie was at her post downstairs, even her usual stolid calm infected by the excitement. She too was be-frizzed, and her big yellow teeth looked unusually protuberant in the unaccustomed frame of cyclamen lipstick.

"Well, I know 'tis upstairs they'll all be going," she pointed out, "but sure there'll be a lot of people here tonight, and there's more room down here like. . . ."

Her efforts were rewarded, for curiosity and thirst gathered the intending patrons in the public bar at an early hour. The crowd was a mixed one: for once the Coal Quay was not in the absolute majority. Business people, lawyers, doctors, other publicans, even a representative or two of the "gentry" came through the newly opened back door from the alleyway, and when at last I led the way up the narrow back stairs, they creaked alarmingly at the unaccustomed burden.

In a new yellow uniform which showed up her black curls and green eyes, Doris stood behind my beloved little counter, wearing the expression of Joan of Arc as the faggots were lit.

Paddy, who paid no attention to schedules at any time, was standing in an affected position at the corner of the bar —one hand on his hip, the other holding his White Lady to the light, the little finger cocked stiffly away from the glass. He gave me a wink from a perfectly serious eye, indicating that he would set the "ton" of the place from the very beginning.

Daisy, who was trembling from head to foot, drew herself up and walked over to him.

"Good evening, Mr. Donovan," she said sedately.

"Ah, Mrs. Kelleher," he replied, equally formal, "will ye join me? What can I be after offering ye?"

Into the total silence of the room, which was already half-full, came Daisy's reply, "The usual, for me, thank you, Mr. Donovan. A Pimms No. 1."

Doris's sigh of relief was audible as she recognized the title of the drink—and everyone gathered around the counter and began talking at once.

Suddenly my astonishing and delightful friend, Tom Flynn, stepped forward.

"Stop!" he exclaimed dramatically, in the tones of one who forbids the banns. "We must do this thing properly."

From the pocket of his plus-fours he drew a baby bottle of champagne with a long pink ribbon tied to it.

"Hold this, Daisy," he said, handing her the end of the ribbon. He looked quickly around the room, then drew a chair near the old-fashioned stone fireplace. "Step up, Daisy," he commanded, and helped her to do so. "Now," he said, "launch the Lounge—ye've seen it on the newsreels, girl. . . ."

Daisy rose to the occasion magnificently.

"I name ye Mrs. O's Lounge," she said solemnly, and let the little bottle swing at the end of the pink ribbon to break neatly into the fireplace.

I nearly wept.

Then Doris really started to work, and I popped behind the counter to help her. Happily, they were mostly a conservative crowd, and preferred to start on straight drinks. As one customer put it, "Ye have to get on with the bread-and-butter before ye're fit to go for the cake."

The Irish will celebrate anything wholeheartedly, and it matters little what the purpose of the celebration may be. That evening, anyone strange to the ways of the island would have thought on entering the pub that some occasion of national importance had gathered the joyous crowd together. Every face reflected pleasure and excitement; the air tingled with gaiety.

The regulars all managed somehow to find the price of a "lounge" drink, made it last as long as they could, and then finished the evening downstairs, talking about it. Although I knew curiosity and interest in a novelty were mainly responsible for the size of the crowd, I felt that there were also genuine friendship and well-wishing in the "Good luck, Mrs. O' " that I heard so often that night.

It was one of those charmed evenings a publican dreams about: everyone drank a great deal, enjoyed themselves, and behaved perfectly. The new customers were friendly and unpretentious, and the old faithfuls only showed their best side.

As it grew later, Tommy, the gadget-player, was persuaded to run home and fetch his instrument, and the singing began. They sang lilting Ceilidh tunes, and sentimental ballads, jigs, and Gaelic laments—all slightly off key, and with immense feeling. No Italian opera star could have covered a wider range of emotions.

When the Garda, somewhat awed by the new splendour, tiptoed up the stairs at closing time, they were made as welcome as they usually were downstairs. Their presence inspired Eddie, who had once been on a day-trip to Calais, to burst into the "Marseillaise." The Irish have a quick ear, and soon his splendid rendering of the words was drowned in the chorus that took up the tune. I was merry enough to respond by intoning in an impossible key the first few words of the national anthem of free Ireland—"The Soldier's Song."

Three of those present, excluding the Guards, had worn uniform—only one had actually been in combat—the entire room echoed to martial sentiments as glasses were waved in time with the song:

> *So-oldiers are we*
> *Whose lives are pledged to I-er-land* . . .

The Guards were even more tolerant than usual, and it was nearly four o'clock when Doris, Bridie and I, locking up wearily, heard a faint snore. We ran it to earth under a settle in the public bar. Paddy Donovan lay in the sawdust, his legs neatly crossed at the ankles, his hands folded on his breast in the manner of a crusader's tombstone effigy. His fingers held loosely, instead of cross or dagger, an upright cocktail glass, the frosting still adhering to the rim and half the fatal White Lady sloshing gently in rhythm with his breathing. It seemed a shame to disturb such peaceful, somehow prim, sleep, so we took the glass away, stuck a pillow under his head, and, hoping that his awakening would not be too painful, tiptoed out.

Fatigue had drained the exhilaration and the satisfaction from me, and I drove home tired and depressed. From the moment of awakening I had felt the surge of excited anticipation of a child on the day of some long-promised treat: all day I had been keyed up for his arrival: every opening door, every greeting called had made me jump and catch my breath. Now I felt quite sick with disappointment. The years piled up behind me in an immense rubble-heap, waiting only for me to move before crushing me in a landslide of weariness. There was absolute blankness ahead, mockingly picked out with small patterns of futile endeavours and fruitless triumphs. I only wanted to cry, and I was too tired even for that. Besides, there is cold comfort in crying alone.

The stairs seemed endless, but when I reached my landing, my slumped shoulders straightened and I paused in surprise and alarm—my front door was open and all the lights were on. Had I not been exhausted beyond consecutive thought, I should have crept away and called a policeman. I stood there for a moment trying to collect my wits, and then all the sorrow and fatigue dropped away from me, for Sean stood in my doorway, laughing, with his arms open, and I ran to them.

10 ⁘ Borrowing Time

"I'm not the man to make trouble for anyone, Mrs. O'," said Paddy Donovan one morning. " 'Tis against me principles. Sure there's enough weeping and wailing and gnashing of teeth in this sad old world of ours, without me being after adding to it."

He looked stern and troubled, like a Biblical elder who has discovered someone milking someone else's goat on the sly. I realized he was building up to something, so I just nodded agreement.

"But," he went on, "when I see someone after biting the hand that's fed them—and that me friend's hand, too—I feel 'twould be wrong to keep it to meself."

"Who's been biting whose hand?"

" 'Tis that Billy Flannigan—the no-good feller—he's doing ye a power of harm, Mrs. O'."

Billy Flannigan, the pride and joy of my most faithful shawlie, was one of the tougher corner-boys and had an unsavoury reputation, even in Cork where the unemployed are often driven to hard shifts. A publican, however, is not in a position to be choosy about his customers. So long as they behave themselves on the premises, he must accept their presence regardless of the stories he may hear about them. So far, I had never seen Billy drunk, and he owed me no money, so I was surprised at Paddy's warmth and his tone of righteous indignation.

"What's he been up to?"

" 'Tis borrowing money from yer customers, he's been, Mrs. O'. Sure, who'd drink regular in a pub when they know they're going to be touched there?"

I checked up on Paddy's story, found it to be true, and realized I should have to take some action. Next time Billy shambled in, I told him I couldn't serve him—and why I couldn't.

"There's plenty more pubs," he said cheerfully.

I was relieved at having got it over so easily.

That night we were kept very busy in the public bar, and I came out from behind the counter to collect empties from the tables. As I returned, bearing my load of glasses, I had to thread my way among the customers standing around the bar. Suddenly I felt my back hair seized and my head was pulled back so sharply I thought my neck would break.

At the same time I heard Mrs. Flannigan's slurred voice in my ear: "So ye'll not serve me boy, ye witch? 'Tis larning ye I'll be!"

And with this she gave another tug. My arms full of glasses and my eyes fixed willy-nilly on the ceiling, I deliberated for a split second. Shout for help? Kick her on the shin?

Still in that absurd position, I said quietly and viciously, "I shan't serve you any more, either. And what's more, unless you're out of this pub within thirty seconds, I'm sending Mike there to call the Guards."

It had happened so quickly that practically no one had observed the incident and those nearest to us were paralysed with interest and indecision. As I spoke, however, Mike, the carter from Upton, who had been a good friend since the belt episode, suddenly came to life and moved closer.

With one of the lightning changes of face of her kind, Mrs. Flannigan threw herself at my knees, tears running down her face, abjectly imploring me to let her stay.

" 'Tis right ye are about Billy," she wept. "He's bad and I know it—but where would I go, sure? Twenty years I've been coming here—please, please, Mrs. O' . . ."

I conquered the nausea that rose in me. I knew she really had no life outside the hours she spent in the pub, and I felt she had had a salutary fright that might ensure protracted good behaviour, so I grunted, "All right, then . . ." and went upstairs to recover my calm.

Doris was arranging some chrysanthemums in the cocktail bar, humming to herself, and I noticed with pleasure that she had dusted and tidied everything and polished the glasses. The fire in the grate burnt brightly, and my spirits rose.

She poured me a drink and then clapped her hand to her forehead.

"There's a letter for ye, Mrs. O'. It came this afternoon, but I was after forgetting to give it ye."

She handed me a mauve envelope. The handwriting was large and wobbly copperplate and the ink purple. I almost sniffed it for violets. I read the note it contained:

Dear Mrs. O',
    If ye have time tomorrow for a small bisness talk, will you let me know.
                    With kindest regards,
                            MOLLY FAGAN

I had a fair memory for names, but it took me some minutes to remember the owner of that one—and then I recalled my first meeting with Daisy, and the man with the wonderful waistcoat; I was back in her snug and saw again the little hunchbacked woman with the sweet smile who had taken no part in the conversation. Yes, I remembered her —but what on earth could she want a "small business talk" about?

I decided to send a note for her over to Daisy's, fixing a meeting time for the next day.

It was earlier than I had arranged to meet Molly when I went over to Daisy's, for I felt curious and knew that Daisy would provide the information I wanted. I was greeted with the usual warmth, and offered tea, stout, and chips, which I refused, and a small dropeen of the crathur, which I accepted.

There were no customers at the time, and we sat in the snug with Eilie and Timmy. No one in Ireland ever considers that there might be subjects which one does not discuss in the presence of the young, and after the early weeks of self-consciousness about it, I had forgotten to care.

"Daisy," I said, "tell me about Molly?"

" 'Tis the great girl she is. Well, 'tis a sad story, ye know. Molly was terrible pretty but at fifteen she got sick wid this polly-o and 'twas given up entirely she was. Only she lived after all but she was a cripple. Her back was twisted up and ye can see she has one leg shorter than the other."

"How sad. Is she married, Daisy?"

"No, but shure she could have been—even crippled and all. She had plenty men after her, but she said no to them all. Ye see, she thought 'twouldn't be fair to a man to burden him with a cripple—and there might be children, too."

Remembering the Madonna-like smile of the woman, I could understand her deformity counting for little with a man, but I was intrigued by her strength of character in refusing the offers of marriage. Hard enough, surely, to bear the burden of disfigurement without that of a self-imposed loneliness as well? And from the purely material viewpoint —keeping herself must be far more difficult than a normal person would find it.

"What does she do for a living, Daisy?" I asked.

" 'Tis loans she's in. Sure Molly's the best in the borrowing in Cork."

This made no sense to me at all.

"How do you mean, loans?"

"Yerrah, everyone needs a little money sometimes, and lending it is big business. Molly does well because no one would make a fuss and refuse to pay when a poor cripple woman might be after getting the sack for it!"

So I learned to my surprise that the overwhelming majority of the Cork people were constantly in debt to the money-lenders, borrowing any sum from a few shillings up to many pounds, and then paying it off in weekly instalments with interest so high, it staggered me. Many, indeed, had several loans going at the same time and some quick mental arithmetic made me shudder at the few coins that could only be left after these drains on the pay-envelopes.

While Daisy was still telling me about the loans—and thoroughly enjoying reeling off the names of my customers who regularly depended on them—Molly arrived, dead on time. As before, she was neatly dressed in a dark coat and a nannyish hat. She carried a red ledger and a bound note-book.

Daisy's welcome was as effusive as ever, but shorter. She then appointed herself chairman of the meeting by settling down at the head of the table, pudgy palms together in an almost pious attitude, and started the ball rolling with: "Well, girl, what are ye wanting with Mrs. O'?"

With a most unCork-like clarity and conciseness, Molly explained. The firms she worked for were handling as much business as they could manage, and there were a number of would-be customers on her route who could be regarded as prospective "regulars." Was I interested in investing?

I was speechless. Me—a money-lender—a Shylock? I was on the point of blurting out an indignant refusal when I looked at the thin face, the sweet mouth, and I thought of the need which dictated recourse to "the loans." I swallowed my pride, and with her calm eyes fixed on me, I thought for a moment. I was in a position to do what she suggested—and suddenly I saw how I could have my cake and eat it, too.

"Molly," I asked, "what's the return per hundred pounds loaned out?"

"Ye can't work it out that way, Mrs. O'. It snowballs, ye see, but ye're always lending out some of the interest that's coming in. 'Tis a sound venture. . . ."

"All right, then—there's a new firm now. We split the profits."

"But shure," she protested, "I've no money to put in, Mrs. O'!"

"Well, I'm not putting in any work. That's fair enough."

I felt suddenly rather naughty—like Phelan. It was pretty dreadful to go in for lending money, but it would be fun to see the profits go where they could do the most good. I remembered my little burglar's poverty, his longing to abandon his heart-breaking profession, and thought that even a very small regular income would help. Through this internal casuistry I reconciled my revulsion with the deed, and felt no further qualms.

Molly seemed delighted out of all proportion, until I realized that her normal commission was unbelievably small and the new venture promised a very real improvement in her circumstances.

Daisy, of course, always ready to celebrate, sent out for the usual lethal chips, despatched Eilie to put the kettle on, and as she poured me the inevitable Paddy, she counted the innumerable unhatched chickens she was convinced would spring from my nest-egg.

" 'Tis a grand house ye'll be buying," she said. "One of them elegant ones up Summer Hill—and we'll be sitting on yer grand terrace having tea and looking down our noses at the town—and Molly'll be driving herself around in a car. Sure, wasn't it the *grand* idea I had?"

"Daisy," I said, "was it you who laid this deep, dark plot?"

The green eyes twinkled and her fat shoulders shook as she replied, " 'Tis feathering me own nest I was—with me two best friends holding the money-bags, sure I'll never be having to pay up!"

A disturbing thought came to me. "Is it legal?"

Daisy laughed until she nearly cried.

"There's hardly a Guard in Cork not keeping a loan going! That's another thing—ye've got the Garda on yer side already, so they'll all be borrowing from you now!"

This was too much, though, and I specified that Molly would simply do the business in the ordinary way, with no mention of my participation; nor, indeed, unless she wished it, of her own. She nodded agreement, and I was grateful for her quick understanding.

But the irrepressible Daisy had one more shot to her bow.

"I've got the very man for yer first customer, Mrs. O'—what about Billy Flannigan?"

11 ∴ Sun—a Stranger

Sometimes the moment of awakening is one of suspense. There is a feeling that the momentous is about to occur—some dramatic change as pronounced as the contrast between oblivion and acute awareness. One morning, my eyes still closed, I felt this sensation of mounting excitement and as my mind began to clear I postponed the moment of stirring in order to savour the sensation.

My hands pushed back the sheets and I rolled on to my back. It was then that an unaccustomed warmth fell on my cheeks and I opened my eyes to an incredible world of gold.

Sunlight was pouring through my window—not the arrogant, lusty sunlight of the hot countries, but a shimmering wet-goldfish, dream ball-dress light—the luminous quality through the rain-washed air untainted or filtered by a single dust-mote.

Like the children in fairy-tales, I rubbed my eyes. Then I remembered that it was August. Even so, I could hardly imagine the green country in this unfamiliar glow.

It was in great haste that I dressed and went out into a new Cork—glittering quays, sequins on the river and the hills and bogs beyond of a green so intense, so vivid, that it was almost painful. The brewery drays passed, drawn by the beautiful bay percherons, their sleek flanks almost the colour of copper, their neatly plaited tails bobbing waggishly, as though they, too, appreciated the glory of the day.

As I turned the corner into the Coal Quay, two men approached and I saw as they came nearer that one was Tom Flynn—and the other—incredibly, Sean.

Like schoolboys with an unexpected half-holiday fizzing in them, they grabbed me each by an arm, and almost in chorus declared that it was too fine a day for work, and we were going down the coast.

"Get your bathing costume, macushla, and we'll go," said Tom.

I laughed helplessly at the idea of owning a bathing-costume in Cork, and they turned hurt, offended eyes on me.

"Sure, don't ye know that Cork Harbour's the grandest place in the world for a swim, then?"

I was silenced.

Buying a swim-suit in Cork was a novel experience. The salesgirl, apparently "not one for the watther" herself, was at first reluctant to admit that the store carried such an immodest garment at all. Then she produced an assortment of dark woollen objects with legs almost to the knees and high round necks in XXXW sizes—obviously designed with Mrs. Flannigan in mind. Warming to the job, she held these up in front of me, but as nothing was then visible of me except my face and ankles, she started digging around amongst various piles under the counter.

Finally, blushing a little, she came up with a brilliant yellow bundle which she handed to me silently. I unfolded it: it proved to be one of those crinkly stretchable swim-suits bearing a label, "Children—11 to 13 yrs." I tried it on in a decorously curtained cranny in the wall, and although not the sort of thing you see in beauty contests, it covered adequately all it was supposed to.

My purchase made, I rejoined Sean and Tom, who, unable to take the strain of standing nonchalantly near the gents' neckwear counter, had bought themselves brilliant and unsuitable ties.

Before finally leaving the city behind us, Tom insisted on buying some whisky to take with us—a precaution which seemed to me excessive in view of the many pubs between Cork City and Crosshaven, where we were bound—but our spirits were so high that none of us felt like arguing and, prepared for the journey, we set out on the southerly road.

The highway from Cork to Crosshaven winds along beside the river, following its relentless course towards the great harbour. On this exceptional morning, it shone so brightly that the impression I got was of twin rivers running in parallel beds. On either side of these, hills rose steeply and gently in turn, wooded in every shade of green, with bare quarried scars of umber and Chinese white here and there to rest the surfeited eye.

I had travelled this road many times before, but the transformation wrought by the sunlight was complete, and the familiar landmarks of farm, inn and village, came as a surprise—only half-recognized and therefore exciting and new.

In a determinedly holiday mood, I had given Tom the wheel, and sat between him and Sean, feeling on my left the warm pressure of Sean's side and the hardness of leg muscles never fully relaxed. I could have sat there forever in the blankness of content, but the irrepressible Tom was for "making a day of it" and, at Carrigiline, we made the first of a series of brief but refreshing stops. Rosie, who knew us as frequent after-hours' "travellers," although surprised to see us at a legitimate time of the day, made us welcome.

As we sat by the fire—for it takes more than a couple

of hours of sunshine to warm the old buildings—I remonstrated with Tom about his purchase of whisky—absurd if he intended to stop at every pub *en route*.

"You must guard your supply lines," he answered. "If you had read your *Von Klausewitz* with any attention, you would think of the long arid stretches with no hostelries."

Finally we got under way again, and after only three more pauses, we reached Crosshaven—the Lido of Cork.

There, the slope up from the water is steep, and on it the great hotel looks out from serried ranks of windows onto the harbour, certainly one of the most beautiful in the world, with its fjords and spreading bays, circled by moor and woodland.

Below the village, on the water, was the swimming club to which Tom hurried us along. I had not really taken the swimming idea seriously and had bought the bathing-suit in the spirit of fun, but the men were quite in earnest, and before I had time to think I was despatched to the ladies' changing room and told to be quick.

When I came out onto the terraced lawns, shivering a little and already doubting the wisdom of such an escapade, I found them waiting there for me—and laughed secretly at the whiteness of their northern bodies. Even after a couple of years of winter, I still had some of the brownness of many suns—but *they* looked as if they were made of icing sugar. A Mediterranean upbringing promotes confidence in the water, and with the gay nonchalance of expertize, I took a running dive into the Irish Sea.

Only by the greatest exercise of will, dictated by the sheer necessity of returning to shore, was I able to swim at all. That water could drop to such a temperature without turning solid seemed impossible. I was blue and shaking when Sean fished me out, laughing, after only a few moments of immersion. He and Tom plunged in and made happy Nordic noises, but even through my misery I was amused to see that they stayed in no longer than I had. As we hurried off to change and warm up, the serviceable tweeds and woollies which I hated drew me irresistibly onwards, and through chattering teeth I mumbled "barbarous climate—uncivilized . . ." and longed for a really savage sunstroke.

Dressed and thawing out on the sunny terrace, passing Tom's bottle around with real appreciation, we watched the traffic in the deceptively warm-looking harbour. There wasn't much of it and our eyes were drawn beyond the occasional small steamer and the tacking sailing-boats to the further confines of the great port.

Crosshaven lies further down the west coast than Cobh, on the opposite bank where the real ocean-going traffic starts, and the water between us and the old Queenstown was untainted by shipping or port filth.

A slow swell emphasized in turn the glaucous green of the northern oceans and their wicked slate blue—utterly unlike the sparkling colours of the Mediterranean, but more alive and beckoning than English waters, on a backdrop of such line and grandeur as to be almost too theatrically perfect. It seemed to call for a Landseer to turn the sweetness into toffee.

The Irish talk a great deal—and so do I—but now we remained silent for a long time, as the blessed whisky burned our throats and poured warmth down our grateful bloodvessels to banish the brief death the sea had brought.

Sean saw me shivering in a last legacy of cold and gently put his arm around my shoulders and drew me near. I looked away from the mountains to smile at him, and as I turned my head, I saw the pain and longing in Tom's eyes, fixed upon me—startling and unexpected. As though in that moment of chance-crossed glances I had asked a question,

Tom raised the bottle to his lips, drank, and smiled ruefully as he answered the silent query.

"Yes, it's the warmth from inside that does it. It has to be there, but you don't know it until you're after being out in the cold. . . ."

His arm locked around me, Sean was far away—his mind with his eyes on the little bleak island over to our left.

"She's well named," he said at last. "Spike Island—a cold little steel spike to spear foolish ambition, to prick the giant bubble of frothy hope, to impale the tortured witch that the inquisitor need not pursue her rising ghost. . . . Did you know, macushla, that that is our very own Alcatraz?"

I shook my head, and he told me in the same quiet, bitter voice, the grim history of the prison lying like a malevolent jewel on the green satin.

As he spoke and I listened, Tom hummed a low eerie tune that seemed to underline the age-old pain of the land. And then, suddenly, the sun withdrew behind the range on the west, and the water turned the colour of steel: Sean stopped abruptly, and threw back his head, screwing up his eyes at the brilliant sky.

I shuddered as Tom's voice sank to an almost tearful note and the melody ended on a half-tone. It was unbearable and I cried out to Tom, "What is it? For God's sake, what is it?"

"Sure, I don't know," he answered. "It comes and goes —may be a lament for lost leprechauns. . . ."

The protuberant eyes in the round childish face (the trim red beard and pointed eyebrows seeming artificial, like a party disguise), went blank as the magic faded out of him, and we stood up in silence and walked to the car slowly; I, with the goose-flesh of contact with the supernatural—the other two somehow flat-looking and empty. The weirdness of those few minutes wrapped me around like a blanket. There was a tightness in my throat and my eyes burned, yet at the same time I was filled with a detached delight and enjoyment. These Celts could express the purest intensity of feeling in spontaneous poetry, and forget it in the same moment, as soon as the overflow of emotion had passed.

The solid, cheerful, frivolous Tom, and Sean, self-possessed, wise and witty, in a few minutes had stripped a dream and a hatred, justified their race, and forgotten the whole thing as though it were no more than a normal act of evacuation—necessary, and completely without interest.

"I don't know why," Tom said conversationally as we entered the car, "but the fresh air and exercise (he had walked about twenty yards that day) always make me thirsty. Let us keep it in the family, my dear Mrs. O', and return to the bright lights of the city and the ministrations of the lovely Doris."

But Sean would have none of it.

"Don't be a glutton, Tom," he said. "There's still enough daylight for a spin along the shores."

Sean drove now, drawn to the places in the Crosshaven area where he had spent his holidays as a boy. We climbed cliff roads, the water a long—too long—drop on one side, and the mountain-side drawing aloof on the other.

Here was the place where he found a deserted rowboat with half a manacle in it—here the deserted church, the ruins where he had sheltered during thunderstorms, guarding his precious burden of sea-birds' eggs—and here a shallow silver-sanded crescent of beach where he had first discovered he could swim.

I wondered, as I listened, at the delight a woman has in hearing her lover talk of childhood joys. The most ordinary recollection of young pleasures acquires a dearness out of all proportion to its interest. Perhaps, I thought, it is because "the child is the father of the man," and in the mould of the early years is the pure pattern of the creature we come to love or hate when the clay has been through the kiln and warped, twisted and cracked ever so slightly.

And, of course, there is a masochistic pleasure in knowing of experience beyond sharing—of the moments of utter contentment in which one played no part. Perhaps this is what contracts the muscles and hastens the pulse in joint longing and resentment—an inevitable renunciation that is almost a reward in itself.

They were ragged musings as each milestone revived a memory for Sean, and the time flew on.

Now the gorse was paling from its yellow glory, and the sea and sky grew darker as the gulls screamed their home-coming. The cliffs softened their angles in sympathy, and the sea-mist began to roll up as we set our faces for home, preceded by the anomalous beams of the headlights—and the harbour began to sparkle here and there with riding-lights.

Sean stopped for a moment. We got out to look a last time on the nearly night-bound harbour. Tom drained the bottle, kissed it, and threw it in a great curve down to the mocking water.

12 ❧ Of a Death and a Drunkard

Daisy's daughter, Ida, died. We all knew she must die, and we knew it would be soon, but still death came with its usual shattering suddenness and the grief prepared for was as violent and demanding as though the impossible evil had befallen. Daisy's suffering was as great as if she had never lost a beloved creature before: her widowhood, the other children dead in babyhood, these had not conditioned her to bereavement or to acceptance; and this time her anguish was the more intense as she had not been with her daughter when she died in the night—alone in the great white hospital, surrounded not by warm human arms and earthy comfortings, but by cool, good, antiseptic figures, speeding on her little soul with murmured Latin politenesses.

The message reached Daisy at dawn, and I was glad that her first instinct led her to me. I awoke to frenzied knocking on my door and found her standing there with the wild mother-tigress look, and before the door was fully opened I knew what had happened. It was moments only before we were in the car and heading for the sanatorium, too late, of course, but as fast as she could will me to drive.

Her wild rush over, her enforced inactivity in the car broke down the tension in her and she wept the tears of utter hopelessness that are so terrifying. It was a nightmare.

My eyes glued to the road, my reflexes geared to the machine, I felt the uselessness, the utter futility of the pain she was enduring, the more cynically maddening as it need not have been. In those horrible few miles I knew that she would suffer so again, and again have earned it, and emerging from it would still be bound to the wheel of her softness and slackness, her refusal to tamper with the only part of her life offered freely to her will.

God! I thought—and then, wryly—yes, God. Leave it to Him, Daisy. Leave everything to Him, what is dearest and most vital, leave your talents and your strength, your freewill and your intelligence. He gave them to you, and you have been taught that "He hath given and He taketh away." How much simpler for you then, not to accept the gifts—instead of using them only to surrender them later! Don't think—don't do anything—that might involve crossing the plans He has made for you. Just take one thing—the suffering He sends you as the rewards for your abstentions. . . .

I had to restrain her from jumping out of the car before it had stopped at the entrance to the hospital, and she ran in ahead of me. I followed slowly, one foot dragging behind the other in the reluctance of my movement. I didn't want to go in, and I knew I must.

Up the wide bare stairway, past the niches with their pastel-plaster saints, each with a nosegay and candles before it, each step more unwilling than the one before, on I went to the end of the passage where a quiet white figure, hands folded on rosary, beckoned me with a nod to enter the small death chamber.

Daisy knelt by the high white cot, her head on the

117

counterpane, her hands running ceaselessly over the quiet limbs of her daughter. There was complete silence. I drew a little nearer and took a sharp breath: the little snub-nosed peasant child with the heavy fringe was gone. In her place lay an incredibly young nun—pure of feature, her brow broad and serene under the severe white coif, her expression solemn and indifferent together. There was no half-smile —the lips were folded firmly together—but neither was there any trace of pain or sorrow, or in fact of any feeling at all. It was another of the terrible contrasts—the agony of the living woman by the bed and the almost contemptuous freedom from emotion of the small corpse, not even pathetic in the remoteness of death.

I stayed awhile in silence, deliberating whether to leave Daisy longer to her vigil, or take her away and attempt to comfort her. The religious standing in the doorway prompted me by a slight nod to leave.

"It does no good," she said as I came out into the corridor, "but a last leave-taking is dear. You cannot curtail it for her. Don't worry, I'll see that she gets a cup of tea in a while, and perhaps you could fetch Eilie and Timmy?"

"Isn't Timmy too young?" I protested. I thought of the tragic, nervous little five-year-old, already following in his sister's footsteps, and my heart sank at the thought of confronting him with this dead stranger.

"His mother would wish it," she replied calmly, quiet reproof in her eyes.

I nodded wordlessly and left. When I returned an hour later with the other two children, they were both already exhausted by crying, and the fact that they had been crying alone, their mother at this time of their need being with the one who no longer needed her.

Full of pity, I left the sad family together. I was told that all the arrangements were in hand for the funeral the next day, and they asked me if I would come back and pick up Daisy and the children later in the day. I agreed, and drove away in a turmoil of sadness and disgust. It was all so utterly wrong, so tragically, wickedly wrong, that I felt physically sick.

The funeral was expensive, as Cork funerals are. Knowing Daisy's usual penury, I willingly paid for it without making any inquiries, but I was amazed once more at the need of the Christian communities of the world for this ostentation in death that somehow seems to comfort them more than any living joys.

The Requiem Mass was said in the hospital chapel. Among the purple vestments, the candles, flowers and incense vapours, the small coffin looked strangely commonplace.

All Daisy's lame dogs, all her regulars and mine were at the funeral, and the huge cemetery wore almost a holiday air as wreath and posy followed one upon the other to do honour to a friend's dead.

Incurably curious, I gazed vacantly at the flowers and began to read the little cards, some blotted, some shakily written, many misspelt. A very small wreath of blooms, slightly wilting already, revived in me the memory of another funeral—one not so well attended; for on the card I read:

> "Suffer little children to come unto Me.
> PHELAN"

It was the fourth time Daisy had returned from the cemetery with her depleted family, and there was nothing I could do to make the journey easier. It was wonderful to find that Molly had got back before we did, and was waiting, warm and sweet and wholly conditioned to the atmosphere of mourning, to give the comfort which I could not.

I took myself off to the pub with a guilty sigh of relief, rejoicing in its humdrum normalcy. It was wonderful to pour stout, make change and polish glasses after the stresses of the day.

Something, however, seemed to be missing or wrong. There was not quite the usual atmosphere, but I put this down to my own heightened sensibilities and the effect of the gloomy day on my customers. It was not until quite late that one of the regulars, having his pint refilled, said casually, " 'Tis a pity about Paddy Donovan, isn't it? Off again. Me missus says that not with all the pledges in the world could ye keep Paddy off the drink when the humour is on him."

Oh Lord, I thought, Damocles' sword has fallen. I had been pushing the thought of Paddy's next orgy into the back of my mind, knowing full well that it was overdue—and now the thing had come to pass.

"Where is it he's drinking?" I asked.

"Over T'Almond Blossom," said my informant.

I called to Bridie and when she came up, I told her in an undertone that she would have to manage on her own for a while, as I had to go out.

Her broad grin took me aback—and I had to laugh when she said, "Ye'll not get anywhere with him, Mam. 'Tis polite to ye he'll be and him promising not to take another drop—and as soon as yer back's turned, he'll be on it again until he can't take no more. But ye'll be afther trying, I suppose?"

I shrugged hopelessly and nodded.

As I went out, I thought I saw a shadow emerge from the lane and follow me. I forgot it at once, though, feeling no fear in Cork, and walked on briskly towards The Almond Blossom—a newish pub not far from mine but in a more "refined" district.

In the public bar, rather chintzy and full of chromium

furniture, there were few customers, and a quick glance showed me that Paddy was not amongst them. And then, with a silent giggle, I realized that he was now such an authority on cocktail bars that he must undoubtedly have gone upstairs, whither I followed.

My guess had been accurate. He was leaning against the counter with a Pimms in his hand, the greenery floating on it so lavish that I felt certain he had directed the barmaid, and a cigar wreathing his head with expensive smoke. He was delivering to the bewildered girl a speech which seemed to be derogatory to the Department of Inland Revenue, and his whole demeanour bespoke a prosperity which seemed incompatible with his circumstances. Had he, I wondered, decided to emulate Phelan, but with his greater gifts of imagination, selected a bank as the object of his attention?

"Hallo, Mrs. O'," he called out, waving the cigar at me in welcome. "Is it a busman's holiday ye're having? Join me and have a Pimms. Sure, Doris does a good one, but Mary here is learning—coming on nicely, eh, girl?"

Humour him, I thought and took a stool beside him at the counter. His eyes were already bloodshot and his hand shook very slightly, although he had only been on the binge a few hours.

" 'Tis celebrating me income-tax refund we are," he explained, winking an enormous wink at me. I thought it more likely that he was celebrating the completion of his period on the wagon. He agreed to compromise and buy me a Paddy instead of the Pimms he favoured, and paid for it immediately. This set the seal on my doubts.

"Paddy," I asked, "have ye come into a fortune ever?"

He laughed gaily.

"I was joking, Mrs. O'. Sure, I've been saving up. While I did your wiring, ye know, and a few other jobs like that."

"Well, I've another job I'd like you to do, Paddy. I

want to add some points and plugs in the flat, and I'd like you to do the job as soon as possible. Could you get the stuff tomorrow after having a look around the place?"

For a moment he looked sheepish, and then agreed. But I noticed he kept his eyes on his glass as he spoke.

Oh, well, I thought, with a job on tomorrow, he'll stop this session tonight, and he'll be no worse than any other man with a hangover.

I bought a round and we chatted for a while, Paddy slurring a little, but still the soul of politeness and good humour, and then I left.

"First thing in the morning . . ." he called after me.

As I walked slowly down the dark street I heard footsteps which matched mine and never grew nearer or further, so that I turned around suddenly.

Caught unawares, the woman stopped dead. It was Paddy's wife, thin, gaunt and very beautiful under the acetylene lamp.

"Forgive me, Mrs. O'," she said, "I didn't want to be stopping ye in public, and I thought I'd wait till we got near your flat to talk to you."

"It's all right, Mrs. Donovan," I said. "Why don't we go into the milk bar and have a coffee together and a talk?"

She looked, I thought, as though she could do with something hot—and may be, I feared, something to eat. She was obviously under some terrific pressure, but she accepted my casual invitation with a poise and calm remarkable in a woman so upset.

Over the coffee and sandwiches she came out with it.

Paddy had pawned all his tools again, pocketed the last pay cheque I had given him (of which his family had not seen a copper), and gone off, as he put it himself, to "celebrate."

She had done as she had been compelled to many times

before—keeping the children, and Paddy, too, for that matter, by doing odd jobs and charring. It was not enough, but it was something.

Furious with Paddy, and full of admiration for her courage, I said impulsively, "Mrs. Donovan, let me help you out until Paddy is on his feet again. I'd like to, really. . . ."

She looked at me in silence for a moment, and then smiled gently as one does at a stupid and well-meaning child.

"I didn't follow you down the street to ask ye for anything, Mrs. O', but to apologize. I know you got Paddy's tools out for him last time—and I know you've given him work you didn't really need done—and you've helped him in other ways. Now he's done this, and I'm ashamed for him.

"There is one thing I'm after asking ye, though—when he's sober again, it'll be to you he'll go looking for work and help. If ye can forgive him, for he'll need it, God knows, will ye please take back from his wages what he owes ye—and then—oh, Mrs. O', could ye pay me instead of him? Sure, he's my man, and good to me, but if you could see the children when he's like this, you'd understand. . . ."

I promised and made a mental vow to see that master Paddy mended his ways—at least as much as pressure could make him.

As we walked home together—their mean rooms were a little beyond my flat—I saw our shadows shorten and lengthen as we passed the street lights, somehow symbolic of the ebbing and flowing currents in the lives of two tired women: one still in revolt against the wrongs and evils that seemed endemic in the soft cool air; the other too beaten for any emotion except acceptance. I could have wrung Paddy's neck.

Even so, I was predisposed as usual to believe in the goodness, however unapparent, of those I liked and enjoyed, and I was convinced that Paddy really would report for duty —if not "first thing" in the morning, as he had said, at least some time the next day. I was determined to be very tough with him and until the evening I kept bracing myself for the lecture he was to receive. Only when it was nearly closing time, and he had not appeared, did I realize that this time was only one of many others, in no way different for my presence from those past—the repetition of a grim pattern not to be twisted by any new influence.

Paddy was not going to "report." His assurances were as valuable as Bridie had estimated—no more. Hurt as I always was by any breach of trust, I felt vicious, and went to the storeroom where I had kept the remainder of the electrical equipment used for wiring the pub. I had bought a number of tools and fittings at the time, not worrying about the extra cost on the basis that everything was usable and in any case saleable if not required.

Of course, there was nothing left. Rolls of flex, boxes of screws and nuts and nails, various screwdrivers, plugs, bulbs, etc., all had gone. I thought, looking at the blank spaces in the shelves, of that Pimms and that cigar. Some rude words, both Irish and Old English, went through my mind, and hastily I took satisfaction in the fact that ill-gotten gains were bound to come to a stop just as soon as others, and then young Paddy would get his just deserts.

But in the meantime, I was exercised in my mind about his family. Again, Molly to the rescue. On learning of the situation, she had at once approached Mrs. Donovan with an interest-free loan. Had I not asked her whether we mightn't do this very thing, I don't think she would have told me; she would have done it and paid the interest herself. As it was, she grinned and said, "Mrs. O', that's what they call a tacit agreement!" And tactful too, Molly, I thought.

And still, for days, Paddy stayed away from home. He slept where he dropped, he spent as he went, and at last his pocket gave out just before his thirst. His credit was non-existent, and he was faced with the choice between Daisy and myself. Daisy was certainly softer, but she knew him better, and even through the haze of alcohol he felt a certain squeamishness about approaching her so soon after her child's death.

So it was into the Daunt's Square pub that he shambled, about a week after the evening in The Almond Blossom, unshaven, unwashed, shaking and red-eyed, but still drawlingly polite, still slurring amiably and still grinning the crooked endearing grin.

"Good evening, Paddy." I greeted him coldly and I hoped in a dignified manner.

"Hello, Mrs. O'—'tis good to see ye again. Sorry I had to keep ye waiting about that job, but 'twas called away I was. Me uncle's after being very ill in the country—mortal dull it was there, too—and me longing to get back to Cork and to work. A pint, please, Mrs. O'."

Before making any attempt to reach for a glass, I said, "That'll be sevenpence, thank you, Paddy."

"Yerrah, Mrs. O'—that was terrible quick! Is it tight ye're getting? Did I ever have a drink in here that I didn't pay for?"

"Lots," I replied briefly. "But I stood them to you. I'm not in the mood for extending hospitality to you at the moment."

His initial astonishment at the turning of the worm gave way to hurt and then to despair.

Wildly he looked around the few customers who were still in the bar, weighing up their possibilities. As he turned his scraggy neck this way and that, he moistened his lips and I could see the thirst in his mouth.

No one looked at him; no one offered him a drink; no one looked as if they would lend him the price of one.

" 'Tis a little short I am of ready," he smiled, "but sure, since you're in such a hurry, I'll make sure ye have it tomorrow, Mrs. O'."

"I have it now, Paddy," I said. "And I'm keeping it. Go home now and nurse your hangover for a day and God help your wife. And when you've paid for your fun, come back and we'll talk about what you owe me."

He burst into tears—slobbering, boozy tears that had nothing to do with remorse, or guilt, or fear at being found out. They were the tears of hopeless, unquenchable desire. He cried, like a child screaming in the dark, for the consolation of drink, and as he slumped over the counter I nearly yielded to the pity he inspired.

But the grapevine works quickly in Cork, and as I teetered on the verge of consent, the door swung open and Mrs. Donovan came in. She smiled at me politely, and taking Paddy's arm with all the tenderness of the world's mothers, she walked him quietly and unprotestingly off the premises.

I wish the story could end there—with a repentant Paddy returned to the fold, and perhaps an increase in his prosperity due to more work, due to some help from me, due to anything. It doesn't, though, and for some time it breaks off completely. It was several months before I heard anything about Paddy other than idle gossip of no import. And what came then must be told in its proper sequence, for it is part of a later and grimmer time in Cork.

13 : Over the Teacups

During the months following Ida's death, I made a point of visiting Daisy as often as possible, and it was with relief and pleasure that I saw her natural resilience responding to time. She accepted her grief, and the acceptance made it easier to bear. It was not very long before she was laughing again in her wholehearted way at the small jokes of daily Cork existence, and her interest in other people's doings never flagged at all.

One morning, when we were in her snug, the old twinkle of curiosity and amusement was in her eye.

"How much petrol is there in your car ever?" she asked.

"Plenty. D'you feel like a spin?"

"Margaret was in town yesterday and told me to come out to their place at Ballinferrig. They've been doing it up ye know. 'Twas in a terrible state when the old man died, but now Pat is back from 'over,' he've turned to and they say ye wouldn't know it. Wisha, I'm dying to see it."

"Let's go now," I said. "It's early yet and we've plenty of time before the evening rush."

I knew Daisy's cosy curiosity and her delight in any novelty, and it seemed to me that a change from the pub would do her a power of good. It was worth having to visit her relations.

We piled into the car—Eilie and Timmy in the back with ample supplies of chips for the journey, and Daisy leaning back happily beside me with her shoes on the ends of her toes and her cigarette dropping ash all over her black frontage. I made all the facetious jokes and silly conversation I could as we went along, because I couldn't help remembering our last drive together, and was praying that Daisy wouldn't. As we passed the station, I said, "That's about the only Irish I know: Stad-na-Trainog."

Daisy laughed, recalling the occasion when, Nature overtaking me suddenly, I had looked at the small notices over two adjacent doors and decided that "Mna" was Gaelic for "Men," only to find to my embarrassment that it wasn't.

The MacNamaras' farm was pleasant and obviously well cared for. The outbuildings had recently been repaired and painted, the land tilled and planted, and Pat and his sister Maggie were delighted with their efforts at redecoration inside the farmhouse. Daisy was enraptured with the cabbage-rose wall-paper they had chosen.

"Now *that's* the sort of paper ye should have put in the lounge!" she exclaimed. "Gay and elegant—and on a rainy day them flowers would be lighting the place up, like!"

I nodded in artificial regret.

We had another of those strange composite Irish meals —a blend of lunch and breakfast and tea—and as we were sitting in the parlour and Maggie was retailing all the local gossip to Daisy's avid ears, Father Flaherty called.

Immediately the "wine" was produced, and the biscuits and the Mud-era cake. Never was there such a flurry of hospitality. All honours were brought forth for the priest. I liked him—he was pleasantly gay and not at all pompous (though I must admit the Irish priesthood usually lack pomposity and are good company). Because I had but recently been "over," he seemed to think that I must share his passion for football, a subject about which I have never known anything at all. Unlike the good Father, who knew every player in every team and expected us to agree with his estimation of each one's worth.

Having had the sense to visit Blarney, I was able to take a little, to the obvious admiration of Daisy and Maggie. There was, however, a quizzical look in the eye of the silent Pat, who could probably, after his time in Dagenham, have given the good Father a lot of information on his pet subject.

Mercifully, the level in the decanter dropped rapidly, and at last, about four o'clock, the priest rose and announced his intention of going home.

Maggie blushed to the roots of her hair, as if about to say something shocking, and in a small voice asked if he'd bless the house before going. He consented cheerfully— rather like a tolerant contralto agreeing to sing "Trees" just once more—and after this departed.

Daisy and I had, of course, risen, too, and we offered him a lift. He laughed and pointed at the smart turn-out in the yard and the fat pony nibbling the bushes.

"He'd find his way home some time, I've no doubt," he said, "but 'twill be sooner if I'm with him. Will ye not come over and have a cup of tea? 'Tis on your way, sure."

Daisy would certainly have committed suicide if prevented from accepting this invitation, and we duly drove at a decorous speed behind the unhurried pony-trap.

The village was a small one, and poor. The dilapidated buildings jostled each other in the sadness of need—need for crowded company if nothing else. But in the middle of the straggly little main street, standing slightly aloof, was a neat, yellow stone building with brilliant green shutters (Works Department Green). Its square front garden was divided uncompromisingly by a cement path: one side was strictly utilitarian and displayed orderly rows of cabbages,

lettuces, shallots and so on; the other half was a geometri
cally perfect pattern of flower-beds in which, as if by some
evil intent, all the colours that could conceivably clash did
in a riot of purples, rust-reds, yellows and pinks.

The pony-trap drew up, and Father Flaherty descended
"Welcome!" he said simply.

As we walked up the path, the door was opened by
a stout, scrubbed-looking, elderly person—the absolute
"dream" housekeeper. Beaming on us hospitably, she pro
ceeded to take the priest's coat, help him on with his slippers
and generally award him the master's welcome. He asked for
tea, and she departed for the kitchen, from which several de
licious aromas were wafted as she slammed the door. The
strongest was that of apple pie.

The parlour was comfortably furnished, and the tea
which shortly arrived, was delicious and lavish. A radio
tuned to Athlone dispensed quiet Irish tunes, the fire burn
brightly (and I noticed it was a coal fire—not peat), and
there were great golden dahlias in a vase by the window. I
couldn't help contrasting the way of life of a parish priest in
Ireland with that of the many priests I had met in other
countries. It seemed to me that the Irish with their whole
hearted way of doing nothing or everything, were deter
mined that temporally as well as spiritually, he should be
above the flock he led. Mentally I reproved myself for think
ing cynically of the very nice man whose guests we were.

Naturally, the conversation, steered by Daisy, turned
towards religious matters and she wanted to know whether
the Father had heard of young Jerry Murphy's going to
Maynooth. He smiled happily at the name. It was many
years, he said, since he had been there, but he would always
remember those as wonderful years.

"I could never understand anyone being unhappy
there," he said. "There were the odd few, but it seemed fan

astic. One curious example I remember—a Corkman—who ailed. Not in the academic sense, I mean, but in faith.

"It was after my time, of course, but it created quite a tir. You might even have heard about it?" He turned to Daisy, who shook her head, and he continued.

"Yes, he was one of the brightest lads ever to enter Maynooth. Suddenly, one day, after only a few months, for no reason that anyone could accept, he declared that he was not going to enter the priesthood after all. His directors, of course, and his friends argued with him and sought the motive behind this incredible decision, but the only answer they got was, 'I simply don't wish to go on with it.' It wasn't weakness, or laziness, or inability to stay the long ardous course—just some sudden and inexplicable change of heart. He left and went abroad immediately, and his parents, who were old and frail, died shortly afterwards within weeks of each other. People said it was because their hearts were broken entirely. I suppose it could be. . . ."

"Of course he came back for the funeral?" said Daisy.

"No, they couldn't trace him at the time. He inherited a fine farm, but it went downhill very fast. You know what tenants can be like if there's no one to watch them. Finally, it was abandoned and if you saw it now, you'd never believe it had been one of the best in the county.

"Strange, that—he was a real loss to the Church. I think I heard he had done well abroad—painting or something like that, and writing—and the other day someone said he has come home to Ireland again. Wish I could remember his name—Sean, Sean . . . Something. . . . Ah, well, now he's back, perhaps the grace will return to him."

My head was in a whirl and I mentally gave myself a shaking. It was too absurd to assume that Father Flaherty was talking about my lover. And yet—so many things seemed to tally.

Suddenly I was back at Tom Murphy's, and I remembered Sean's stiff attitude as the future of young Jerry was discussed, and the expression of pain on his face. Was it possible? The same brick wall of "no questions" was between me and the answer.

After a little more desultory conversation, we left. Daisy had enjoyed her outing, and I had plenty to think about. After dropping her at her pub, I decided not to work that evening, and went home.

I couldn't sit still. Pacing up and down the small drawing-room, I weighed the slender evidence I had. That Sean had travelled extensively, I knew. That he was an artist, I knew, too.

But—he had been in the Cathedral that Sunday of our picnic—and I wondered. Had he abandoned the religious life from altered convictions, surely the entire framework of ritual, the whole pattern would have jarred on him! And yet, if he had made a decision as serious as that, I felt certain it was not through lack of determination or character.

And then—I simply could not imagine Sean with a vocation in the first place. Just as I was dismissing the whole idea as an absurd association of a story incompatible with a personality, I remembered that look of incompleteness, almost of loneliness which had struck me when we first met. How young he had seemed, how every tenderness of our relationship seemed to leave him with a sense of wonder. His newness, his innocence came to my mind. Perhaps in Father Flaherty's story was the key to the strange unfinished quality of a personality which had changed.

For Sean's age showed now, not as a sad accumulation of years to be regretted or accepted with resignation, but rather as an outward manifestation of a maturity which fitted his life. Puzzled and disturbed as I was, I smiled at the thought that this at least was partly my doing. He was no longer a youth in the body of a man. Indeed, he was now stronger, older and wiser than I—and even more lovable than before.

Serene in my certainty that, whatever his past history, Sean was satisfied with a present which included me, I decided firmly to think no more about the question until it could serve some purpose.

But, of course, I went on pursuing the possibilities down rambling mental paths. . . . "I'll take you to another farm one day. . . . You'll understand. . . . Why know anything except what one wants to. . . . Thank you for your discretion. . . ." So many things he had said that began to make sense in this context.

Suddenly I realized that whilst family names in Cork are used more than anywhere else I have been (perhaps because most of the Christian names are so common in the limits of the Saints' Calendar) Sean, who seemed to know everybody and to be well known in his turn, was always alluded to by his first name only. Again I wondered at the odd hesitation, the delicacy, which had always forbidden my making inquiries either of or about him, almost (how ridiculous!) as though I were afraid of learning more than he chose to reveal in the half-unreal present. Perhaps I would have been less shaken to learn of some disreputable episode in his past than of his former vocation.

I longed for him to return to Cork, although I still had no intention of trying to penetrate his barriers. Some chance remarks would surely give me a clue—as if it mattered!

Enough, I thought. This treadmill of useless conjecturing on a theme not even stated is too unrewarding. . . . And having thus resolved, continued to wonder until sleep at last slowed the treadmill to a stop.

14 ⁘ A Night at the Opera

My friend Tom Flynn and his wife, Moira, were usually at loggerheads.

They both had qualities and defects in Irish abundance, and were so suited to each other by birth and upbringing that only real passion could have made a success of their marriage.

They were terribly fond of each other occasionally. For the rest of the time they were a joke to all their friends, who sympathized, and took sides, according to their natures, but were always amused and couldn't resist their curiosity about the latest incident in the comic-strip of the Flynns' relations.

Tom himself was no doubt a trying husband. He drank like a fish (but then in his crowd this is not unusual), womanized if the opportunity arose, and was stubborn and pedantic about the subjects on which he considered himself well informed, in the particularly maddening way of Irishmen.

His wife was pretty, spoiled, a virulent snob, and unfortunately deeply in love with her brother—a nasty young man.

When we met the Flynns separately, we used to ask them, "Is Moira in Cork?" or "Is Tom away?" as a matter of course, for there were constant hair-raising scenes in the middle of the night as suitcases were flung out on to the path in front of their smart little villa "never to return."

I was delighted when Moira, beautifully dressed as usual, and looking cool and serene, strolled into the pub one Saturday morning and invited me in her usual casual way to "come to the Opera tonight."

"We've got a box," she said, "and I just met Sean and asked him, too. He said he would if you would."

I accepted at once, and she said to come over early and have drinks and small things to eat because "the Opera starts at the most uncivilized hour." With great self-restraint I refrained from asking what the Flynns were celebrating together in this remarkable way.

I knew there was an Opera House in Cork, and had in fact often passed the domed building. I remembered being impressed with the fact at the time when, shortly after my arrival, I was immersed in a little book called *A Short Story of the Irish Race.* The author, quoting Sir William Petty, tells us that in 1655, with "three-fourths of the population living in cabins that had neither chimney nor door nor window, and sustaining themselves on a little milk and potatoes . . . it is a striking testimony to the spirit and the ideals of the Irish people that these creatures huddling in these huts and just trying to cling to life, should at the same time merit censure from this Englishman for that as he states: 'The superior learning among them is a philosophy of the schools and the genealogies of their ancestors.' "

Sir William also found in the remote mountains of Kerry "not only people who knew French, but to his astonishment [found] that Latin was spoken even by very poor men."

With this picture of Irish culture in mind, it had seemed to me, at the time of reading this, quite natural that there should be an Opera House in Cork, and I had then forgotten all about it. Opera has always left me comparatively cold as a form of entertainment and, purely acoustically, I preferred instrumental music to the human voice. In any case, I had been very busy in Cork and had never felt inclined to seek amusement or elevation in any of the public places. I was interested, however, in this opportunity to view Cork's *Kunst* at close quarters, and in such diverting company.

The evening proved one of varying moods and atmospheres, and began on a note of comedy.

As we knocked on the Flynns' door, and stood waiting, an unearthly racket exploded within: voices were raised, and there were two loud crashes as of disintegrating china—then complete silence.

"Stand aside, macushla, before the bags sail out of the door," Sean grinned.

Moira let us in, ravishing in emerald-green velvet the exact shade of her eyes—smiling a hostess's gracious greeting.

As we peeled off hats and coats, Sean asked gently, "That sounded like an exciting play on the wireless, Moira. What station are you tuned to?"

"We haven't got the radio on—that was just the savouries. Tom wanted to put them on the sideboard (he's so stuffy and bourgeois), and I wanted to put them on the coffee-table."

With bated breath we waited for the dénouement. But Moira said no more about it, and led us disappointed into the drawing-room. Then we realized that a late supper after the Opera would be essential. The room was impeccable, and in the fireplace, where a splendid log fire burned brightly, were the remains of two large dishes. Sizzling a little, and blackening at the edges, were the savouries.

Our host sprang to his feet and began to dispense drinks.

"I was wondering which would go best with these," he beamed, "anchovy, or *pâté*—and then the artist in me was revolted by both of them. . . . A little more soda?"

Gazing on us kindly he waved us to seats and handed us our glasses.

Sean leapt into the breach.

"What's the programme tonight?" he asked.

" 'Fanny by Gaslight.' "

I sat up straight. This promised to be interesting.

"Who did the score?" I inquired.

Tom gave me a quizzical look.

"Yerrah, I don't know," he said. "It'll be on the programme."

Pleased anticipation filled me, and as we took our places in the red plush box, I felt that even on a seat as hard as the one I occupied, I was going to enjoy myself.

The lights were already dimming as we sat down and I couldn't read the programme. The auditorium was full and the usual coughing and settling-down noises all but drowned the orchestra, which, I noticed suddenly, was playing a medley of World War I favourites. This struck me as rather an original idea—period music to open a period programme—even if the periods didn't quite overlap. From the size of the orchestra, it was obviously not going to be a full-scale performance, and the wisdom of presenting an authentic opera in a provincial town without extravagance, impressed me.

The curtain rose on the familiar opening scene: the empty living-room, the severe Victorian marble fireplace, the gas brackets on either side of it, the formally arranged parlour furniture.

Suddenly I realized that I was about to see "Fanny by Gaslight" exactly as it had first appeared—not transformed into an opera at all. I repressed a giggle and shot Tom a reproachful glance. I was bitterly disappointed—"Fanny" would have made such a splendid opera!

However, the play had its compensations, for half the

repertory company was English and the remaining characters had rich full brogues. Fanny herself was a stand-in that night, and her rendering of the blood-curdling leading part was pure Coal Quay. Sean was helpless with laughter from the first few minutes onwards, and when the first curtain fell, I was aching.

The Cork Opera House, which is used for any and every dramatic purpose, is equipped with the largest and fullest bar I have seen in any theatre—and there are twice as many curtains introduced into every performance as originally planned by the dramatist. I found this to be a good thing—the legs have no time to develop pins and needles, audience and actors are kept in a lively mood, no matter how dreary the play, by constant trips to the bar, and the management is happy, too.

Tom told me there are many regular patrons of the Opera House who have never even seen one act of a play there. The only people who have ever been heard to criticize this arbitrary chopping-up of the drama are those who "have the pledge taken"—and for them there are always the ice-cream and chocolates men.

After the play and its six intervals, we were all in high spirits and extremely happy. By then, I knew there was little chance of our getting anything to eat except at the cinema restaurants, to which I had the aversion of the claustrophobic and the elbow-bender, as these establishments are both crowded and dry, so I suggested bacon and eggs at my flat. This was agreed to with enthusiasm, and we set off, Sean and I arm-in-arm, and Tom clutching Moira's shoulder—partly from the affection he always showed her between rows, and partly because she afforded solid support after an evening's gentle but persistent drinking.

Over the meal we laughed about the play and Tom

admitted to having deceived me as to the nature of the entertainment.

"But shure," he crowed, "I wanted to see your face—and it was worth it."

Moira sat on the floor, her legs curled under her, leaning against her husband's knees: all was calm and pleasant, and Sean asked innocently, "Sure, you haven't told us what we're celebrating?"

Airily Tom said it was still early, the night was young, it was in fact only one A.M., and please could he have another whisky?

Sean took his empty glass and refilled it.

"Nothing like a good fire and a good drink—in good company, of course," said Tom sententiously. "You don't realize how precious these small things are until you've actually faced and conquered hardship. . . . Now, when I was in charge of the defence of Shannon Airport. . . ."

The three of us interrupted with protesting groans.

Every time Tom had had one too many—and this happened at frequent intervals—his martial sentiments came to the fore. It was his misfortune that his blood and upbringing had fitted him for the life of a soldier; and when a splendid war had turned up at just the right time, he had been a neutral in a neutral country.

His brother had died at Singapore, serving with the British Forces, and been posthumously decorated for conspicuous gallantry; but Tom had been compelled to remain in Ireland and run the family business. His military career had been confined to extensive reading of military handbooks and monotonous, if well-moistened, drilling near Shannon.

We all knew how rosy his recollections of this period were apt to become, and in fact each of us was familiar with several versions of the stories, more or less highly coloured, according to the degree of his intoxication.

Tonight, he was at the "intelligence" stage, and waving our interruptions aside, he continued, "Naturally, as a captain I was a fairly junior officer, and when I insisted that the only feasible plan was based on Von Klausewitz's octagonal and semi-deployed——"

Moira's green eyes began to look vicious, and without warning she said, "You bloody liar."

Tom's heavy lids continued to droop lazily over the blue eyes. He sighed and said quietly, "The little woman is a trifle tense—only natural. You asked what we were celebrating—well, there is to be a 'little stranger.' We are in the family way."

Moira whirled on him. "We—hah!" She spat the words.

"Trying to keep it in the family, dear?" Tom cooed. "Too bad you can't give your dear little brother the credit for that, too."

Sean managed to whisk their plates away into the kitchen like greased lightning, but Moira still had her glass. She got up, threw the contents in her husband's face, and ran out of the flat.

Tom waited a moment, drew out his handkerchief and mopped his face and then walked quietly to the window and out on to the balcony. We watched in stunned silence. He waited until the door below slammed, and as Moira, coatless, hair flying, emerged like a green fury from the house, he solemnly poured his drink over her.

Smiling pleasantly, he re-entered the room.

Extending his glass silently to Sean, he looked at me quizzically: "I wonder whether you'd mind, my dear, if I used your sofa tonight?"

With Sean there, I didn't mind—and as he nodded I agreed and went to fetch blankets. We put pillows on the sofa and, as if Tom were a small child, the fire-guard in front of the fire. Sean put the two decanters and a glass at his elbow.

Since our guest was already snoring gently, I asked why the drinks? Surely he would sleep the sleep of the dead now until morning?

"Don't you know, darling, when a man is as deep in debt to liquor as Tom is, he can never move far away from it? If he awoke and found nothing to hand, the realities would send him mad. He'll need it, don't you doubt it."

"Oh, Sean," I said, "I'm so sorry for them—for both of them. Isn't there anything that could be done about them? If only Moira wouldn't be so bitchy. . . ."

"And if only Tom didn't make her so unhappy that she need be," he replied. "Moira's the worst off really. Tom can drown it, and he can give other women the eye. Moira can't even admit what ails her to herself—and Tom knows it, and though he hates it, he uses it to torture her."

"They're both Catholics, aren't they?"

He nodded.

I sighed, for indeed, there was no way out.

15 ❧ Reflections on a Sickbed

I had been in Cork for a full year when I developed a very painful, if harmless, form of tonsillitis, and found myself for the first time since my arrival entirely alone for several days. This is not to say that my girls and Daisy didn't visit me daily and that I was not looked after. But it was the only occasion when I had had literally hours on end of thinking time at my disposal—and a very strange and pleasant feeling it was.

Idle by disposition, and active by chance and choice, during this period I was able to indulge myself without offending my sense of duty or fidgeting through excess of energy.

Surrounded by the books I had been meaning to read for months, a couple of new albums of records to hand, I luxuriated in an atmosphere of Friar's Balsam and whisky in medicinal but frequent doses. Oddly enough, however, I read little during this indisposition, and seemed to spend most of my time taking stock of the events of the past year—pondering their causes and consequences, idly reviewing incidents which had come and gone too fast for contemplation. Perhaps the slight intoxication of fever made me more imaginative than usual—or at least thrust out of mind all the small daily preoccupations that normally obscured inner vision.

I looked back on the year with deep gratitude and content, mixed with amusement. It had been a year of discoveries and small triumphs, of minor disappointments and delightful surprises. Generally, the black figures overwhelmed the red. Tenderly I thought of Sean, to whom I owed the deep joys; and somehow, in the same moment, I realized that it was to the country itself—no, to the county—that I was indebted: that Sean represented it to me in its most exciting and lovable form; he and its climate seemed inextricably fused in my life, as though to imagine the one without the other were impossible. His secrets were those of the dark country—his moods those of the weather, shadowed and silent and then suddenly unbelievably radiant—his love was the love of a race, a nation—and his sudden absences, unexplained and unjustified—they were the lapses in the charm of Ireland.

Perhaps his faults, which I seldom saw, were also those of the bigoted, narrow-minded, slovenly Irish. They would not have affected my feelings for him any more than they alienated me from his fellows. If they had made me furious—and had I really seen them, they would have done so—I would have felt the anger that is closely linked with love, the anger of the irritated mother, the near-hatred of passion. Again, as I thought of his slow smile, of his voice and his clever, gentle hands, I felt the usual almost superstitious shudder of pleasure—an unconscious knowledge of holding and keeping something not really mine, astonishingly allowed to me for a little while.

My thoughts ranged around the area of my daily life. I saw again my uncertain beginnings in Cork. My doubts and fears revived, and I shivered at the memory of the emptiness that was in me when I came there.

Gratefully I regarded the many friendships—the absence of enmities—that summed up a year of close contact with people who had been strangers. If I had learned little of Ireland's cultural and spiritual life, I had absorbed, almost by osmosis, the feeling of the people. I had been accepted in the undefined way of real acceptance—by no statement or contract—without any effort save that of understanding even when this seemed beyond the limits of will and intelligence, and could only be done through the heart.

It was at this point of my musings that I realized how inarticulate are the tongues with the gift of the gab—clattering along with the same old Blarney noises, expressing only the preconceived and predigested ideas, until their clarity comes from the words they don't understand, the ones they produce like magic and that set them apart by some mystical transformation in an ambience entirely their own.

These were the delights of Irish experience: the unwilled wealth of sensibility, superstition, belief and cruelty; the tenderness that a tone of voice and an inflexion revealed; the fantasy of spirit in an ungrammatical inversion of speech; the supreme humanity of an utter faith in good cohabiting in perfect comfort with habitual indulgence in evil—a humanity like well-water beneath the heavy sod of ignorance.

Perhaps I could have found elsewhere the same unquestioning acceptance of existence, the same unquerying attitude of mind. They never considered the nature of things—philosophical and metaphysical thought was prohibited both by their poverty and their faith. But somehow, through their very lack of interest in these things, their psychic qualities seemed to appear more clearly to me, and they had kept the elements of fantasy which colour all the world's childhood—the imagination of the very young remains with the grown Irish so that one may hate or love them but never find them dull.

For no particular reason, I suddenly thought of Mrs. Flannigan, still fawning, cheating, tippling, liable to knife me, true to me in her fashion, ungrateful and fond of me. Everything in the world was wrong with her—and I should have hated it if she had transferred her custom to another pub. I knew she nodded wisely when her unpleasant son voiced his opinion of me (he still nursed his grudge), for she would tell me, "Yerrah, Mrs. O', 'tis wicked the things Billy says about ye—but he'd be after hitting me if I said no." She nodded several times, and put her finger to her lips. " 'Tis wiser to listen and say nothing, always. . . ."

Remembering her solemn face and the *naïveté* of her hypocrisy, I laughed out loud and the pain in my throat, as a fit of coughing ensued, acted as a reminder of Phelan, and I smiled again as I considered my one real achievement in Cork.

For Phelan was a reformed character, and it was partly due to my intervention. Indeed, it was one of the delightfully unlikely blessings of fate that make one feel justified in taking a hand in the direction of other people's affairs. When his twins died, I was new to Cork, and more affected than I should have been later, when death had become a familiar citizen. Therefore, I made a perfect nuisance of myself for a long time afterwards, and finally at a business meeting I scored a strike.

One of the directors at a brewery was complaining, during a boring discussion about rising costs, that there seemed to be no way of stopping the petty pilfering that went on in some of their storehouses.

"You can't get a reliable storehouseman at all," he complained. "If they're not asleep, they're deaf."

"Would ye be the man for a gamble?" I asked, inspiration coming to me.

There isn't an Irishman who won't rise to that one—

even the cautious hard-headed business man. He cocked an eyebrow at me and waited.

"There's nothing like a retired burglar for knowing the ropes," I began.

They laughed and I continued, giving them a brief outline of Phelan's story. There would have been little point in concealing it, for they would certainly have checked up on him. Besides, I had a hunch the mad idea would appeal to them.

"But it hardly seems fair to give a job to a man with a bad record when there are so many honest boys out of work," one of them protested.

"Yes, and them not knowing the difference between a jemmy and a crowbar!" I countered. "Do you really want to put a stop to this thieving or don't you?"

Their sporting instincts won the day, and within a week, Phelan, having sworn to justify the trust we put in him, was installed at the brewery. That no further thefts occurred in his storehouse may have been due to his efficiency or to his popularity with the underworld and its sympathy for him. I don't know.

But day by day his shoulders seemed to straighten; his shabbiness lost its furtive appearance. The glory of the small regular pay-packet was out of all proportion to its size. And when his wife learned from Molly that a small investment he had made years ago was paying dividends which she received regularly, it seemed like a fairy-tale. Particularly as her husband could never remember having been in a position to invest in anything. But Molly was known to have a "good business head," and if she said so, "Well," acquiesced Phelan, "I must have drink taken at the time."

We couldn't cure the tuberculosis, and there was much more we should have been glad to do for the Phelans, but it was a great satisfaction to have been able to take the edge off their sufferings. It was one of the days when I should have liked to feel Molly's confidence and join her in her humble thanksgiving at the Cathedral. Yes, that was one of the pleasant things to remember.

I lit a forbidden cigarette, and poured myself some more of the medicine.

Molly's discretion and thoughtfulness in this matter, as in everything she did, struck me for the thousandth time, and I was reminded of another warming result of the year which had been no less eventful for her than for me.

Her increased prosperity had not gone to her head, and she continued to lead the quiet, dull, devoted life of previous years—with one very significant difference. The knowledge that it was in her power to help people even in a small way gave her a confidence and a gentle gaiety which were new. So well did these become her that the sweet face seemed to grow younger and the misshapen body less noticeable than ever, and one day, when we were going over the accounts together and she giggled during one of the long silences imposed by my weak arithmetic, I half-knew what she was going to say.

"At my age, 'tis ridiculous, Mrs. O'," she began, "but ye know Foxy O'Rourke over the road?"

It was he who had tapped my first barrel of stout— indeed, I should never forget him. I smiled as I waited for what was to follow.

"He's after me to marry him, the fool."

The affection in her voice qualified the opprobrious epithet, and I asked whether she would.

"It's like this, Mrs. O'. Years ago, I wouldn't marry, for 'twould have been wrong—me a cripple and poor, too. But now, sure"—she dimpled—" 'tis a woman of substance I am, and a man could do worse. Besides, he's a good man, and settled in his ways. I'm after getting sorry for him. . . ."

Another happy ending. I was so pleased that I rushed her over to Daisy's, knowing how glad she would be of her old friend's decision. It was worth the indigestion consequent upon the party Daisy put on. Stuffing us with her own choice of luxuries, she chattered on and on about Molly's future bliss, larding her absurd romanticisms with frankly doubtful jokes which the quiet Madonna-like Molly seemed to enjoy quite as much as I did.

Punching my pillow into a more comfortable position, I laughed at the recollection of the announcement of Molly's engagement in the press. Bursting with pride, Foxy had rushed off to insert it and, having become a litle confused between the various forms used, had announced his engagement and requested "no flowers."

No one could have rejoiced more genuinely than I did at Molly's good fortune, but somehow I felt the sadness not of envy but of self-pity. Her dull future with Foxy would have appalled me, but my own was so nebulous I envied her the certainty of her plans. Self-pity thrives on sickness, and I indulged in it for a few lonely minutes until it became so dull that even the image of myself as a lonely deserted woman ceased to be pathetic. After all, it wasn't even enhanced by the glow of novelty. My attention turned again to the lives of my friends, which seemed to take forms so much more definite than mine, and I considered Deirdre, who had now become a perfect bore about baby-books, ventilation and cod-liver oil.

Her delight in the child her servant had wished on her grew greater day by day, and, indeed, it seemed that the baby had inherited none of the mother's oddness and was proving entirely satisfactory.

It was amusing to meet Deirdre panting along the country roads, shoving an enormous pram, her cheeks scarlet, her grey hair blowing around her face, everything about her proclaiming the proud granny or nanny except the glances she gave the sleeping child—these were purely maternal.

"I've cut down on me smoking," she told me one day.

"Smoky rooms are unsuitable for young children. And I walk two miles at least every day—people who stay at home in a fug are liable to develop infectious pulmonary diseases to which infants are very prone."

"Deirdre, how many ounces of sugar of milk do you put in his bottle?" I asked teasingly.

She replied perfectly seriously with the appropriate figures and said that he was liking "lightly boiled eggs now, and sieved vegetables too, God save him!" Heaving a sigh of relief that those delights were not for me, I had hurried home to smoke incessantly and develop any respiratory disease that might take a fancy to my fuggy habits.

Drowsily I worried a little about Daisy, thought sadly of Paddy Donovan, whom I never saw now, half-consciously pushing away the sorrows and troubles of those I was fond of.

A slow-motion carnival of Cork passed before my eyes as I lay in bed, and alternatively I smiled, scowled and sniffed as each character, a little larger than life, a little more brilliant in the grease-paint of reminiscence, bowed mockingly or laughingly at me.

I was standing on the corner outside the pub, and the sun was shining brightly—they trooped past me, from the Coal Quay towards Patrick Street, comical, tragic, clownish —singing *Te Deums*, Jigs, and "Danny Boy"— each stopping to make a deep obeisance as I inclined my head and blessed each one from a gin bottle with a pourer-cork.

Suddenly they backed away in fright, and I couldn't see what they feared. Wildly I turned my head this way and that—and then I felt the hands tighten round my neck infinitely slowly and inexorably. I tried to scream, tried madly to see, at least to see, my assailant, and the hands continued to squeeze and squeeze. . . . I fell as they released me and saw Sean grinning down at me as I lay in the mud—laughing, laughing, rocking with laughter, pointing at my neck twisted like a chicken's, laughing. . . .

16 ❖ Cork Christmas

The sense of being cast out, the chilled, lost, lonely feeling my nightmare left with me, outlived my convalescence, so that, despite the welcome which awaited me at the pub and the solicitude of my friends and patrons, I continued for several weeks to regard each morning with suspicion and anxiety, and to greet each day's end with relief that no blow had fallen.

Sean was still away. This was his longest absence yet and added to my unease. I was in a fair way towards becoming neurotic and hung on to my sense of humour. But it seems to me that there is very little humour in the most comical situation when it cannot be shared and when the ludicrous calamities befall oneself. I was at the lowest ebb, and the winter in surly sympathy closed around us darkly, filling the river to the slimy brim, scattering largesse (with a promise of more to come) to the cemeteries, lowering the levels in the Paddy bottles ever faster.

Advent was upon us, and the pitifully hopeful anticipation of Christmas that sent the threadbare crowds scurrying around the cheaper shops was reflected in me as in some dark mirror or the negative of a film. Instead of optimism and good cheer I felt fear and depression—a sinister awareness of impending sorrow, unlikely by present indications, but as positive as the gloomy prognostications of those with the "sight."

I told myself uselessly that I would be believing in the "little people" next, and bade myself stop brooding. How Irish can you get in a year, girl?

Into this cosy little slough of despond came Christmas, and I mustered up enough energy, albeit reluctantly, to go on a shopping expedition. It seemed absurd to penalize my people for the fact that the season felt ominous rather than festive to me. In fact, my spirits were lightened by the pleasure of selecting gifts.

I enjoyed buying presents either so ideally suited to the recipient that they couldn't fail to please—or so eminently unsuitable that they would never have dared to buy them for themselves. In the first category, I found a wonderful frame for Daisy's family photographs—massive and black, elaborately carved and smothered in mother of pearl. In the second, I could hardly wait to see Molly's face when she unwrapped the frothy negligee, which would certainly delight Foxy.

Pleased with my purchases, and my mood a little brighter, I hurried home on foot. The car was in dock, and in any case I enjoyed being laden like the crowds around me with bulky, oddly shaped parcels which could quite well have been delivered (this would have taken half the pleasure out of the expedition).

It was bitterly cold and unusually dry. My breath smoked and the street-lights shone with an unreal brightness. Somewhere on the way home I passed a night school or some such institution. The windows showed lights, and inside young voices were raised in the *Adeste Fideles*. Suddenly I started to cry, not the quiet tears one can blink away and pretend never happened, but the choking, sniffling, nose-reddening sobs of childhood, forlorn, heart-broken with the certitude that such misery could never stop. Weeping *comme une Madeleine, comme une fontaine* I marched on—my arms full, unable to blow my nose, and not caring anyway who witnessed my foolishness. It was one of those moments when one needs a nanny and a hot-water bottle, and I had neither. Merry Christmas to me! I gulped as I threw the parcels onto my sofa and flung myself face down on the bed.

It was late next day when I awoke from the sleep of sheer exhaustion, and I dragged myself to the pub. I felt guilty at the amount of time my sickness and subsequent self-indulgence had kept me out of the bar, and because of the additional work this had meant for the girls. On the impulse, I gave Bridie the day off. Her pleasure in the unexpected outing was reward enough, and I felt, too, that a good work-out in the public bar would get rid of my "vapours." She went off with a promptitude she had never displayed before; I settled down behind the counter. It was only eleven, and the bar was empty—the early morning market rush was over, and the pre-holy-hour drinkers had not yet started to trickle in.

I was bending down to the slightly loosened spigot of the Guinness cask when I heard the door open and "Top of the morning to ye, Mrs. O'!"

It was a perfect imitation of Paddy Donovan, but only one voice could have said it that way. I whirled and ran out from behind the bar.

"I should be showing you the door," I gasped. "All this time and not a note, not a word—you pig!"

"The words are all stacked up waiting for you, mavourneen. It has been as long for me as for you. But there's plenty of time now, for I shan't be going away again. . . ."

Speechlessly, I leaned against his shoulder, rejoicing

in the hard muscles and the roughness of his fisherman's sweater—completely forgetful of all the sadness and fear—content as I always was with him.

Suddenly I realized that I had no one to leave the pub with and that I was tied for the whole day. Dolefully I said, "Hell!" and his eyebrows lifted.

"Not you, you fool." I explained, and he laughed.

"Don't fuss so, darling. There's no hurry. I notice ye've done nothing about the festive season?" looking around with mock disapproval.

Accusingly, I replied, "I didn't feel festive."

"But you do now . . . I'll be back in half an hour," and before I could say anything he was gone.

He was true to his word and kicked the swing door open as he came in, hardly visible over the boxes and parcels he carried. He dumped them on the bar.

"Get the step-ladder like a good girl," he ordered, and as usual, I obeyed dumbly.

The rest of the day was spent putting up tinsel, silver balls, streamers, paper-chains, anything and everything that could be called a Christmas decoration.

I giggled helplessly at the thought of Mrs. Flannigan under the vast bunch of mistletoe Sean thoughtfully hung in front of the till; the upside-down whisky bottles took on a roguish look with their bottoms festooned with holly; the casks looked like snowdrifts of cotton-wool and artificial frost.

He disappeared briefly in a direction that called for no comment, and then yelled dramatically, "Come and see the Gents!"

In brilliant chalks on the narrow whitewashed wall he had drawn a straddling Santa Claus with his back to us, winking over his shoulder. The caption ran: "Compliments of the Season—many happy returns."

The customers who had collected during the day thoroughly enjoyed participating in our preparations and the day grew progressively more joyous—until finally, disentangling ourselves from the last bits of holly and cotton-wool, we realized there was no tree. Nothing would do for Sean but to get one at once. I protested, but he took the car and went off.

At closing time, he had not returned and I grew anxious.

At nearly two o'clock he arrived and my relief when he staggered in under a sizeable fir was immense. He looked white and tired—I put it down to the cold and the exertion of felling and carrying the tree. In a way, I welcomed his slight indisposition as a chance to care for him, to warm him with hot whisky, and mother him a little. He quickly brightened up and I stopped worrying. We went home tired but very happy. All my miserable forebodings seemed to have disappeared and I looked forward to Christmas with the wholehearted joy of a child.

As though the weather were determined to reflect my own inner climate as it had done so faithfully since I arrived in the island, a real white Christmas materialized, giving the whole county the air of a Walt Disney cartoon. The low bushes grew soft and lumpy, like cotton-wool, all outlines became rounder and more stylized, the clear Irish complexions reddened by the cold were more reminiscent of Snow White than ever—not blimpishly ruddy but "white as snow, red as blood, and black as ebony."

There was something absurdly cosy about the frosty white scene—reducing sizes to nursery proportions and making one forget the misery of unheated hovels, the outsides of which, like iced cakes, seemed new and lovely.

We threw ourselves into this most wonderful of all Christmases with our whole hearts. It was too late to make puddings, but we bought the most beautiful we could find and soaked it for days in brandy. The turkey Sean proudly brought home was far too large for my bachelor oven, but the baker was obliging and roasted it in his great one, so that to its own inimitable scent of stuffing and crisp golden crackling was added the slight tang of fresh-baked bread.

For the small flat we found a small tree and lovingly made it as pretty as we could, carefully grouping around it the presents for our friends. Unshared Christmases are too sad to be noticed. I had ignored so many that this one, centred on the presence of Sean, was as thrilling for me as if I had never enjoyed it before.

One part of the holiday that I had always loved, regardless of moral or philosophical implications, was the Midnight Mass and the *Réveillon*. I didn't know whether Corkonians revelled on Christmas night—but I was going to, and those of our friends who joined us were going to also.

Slightly hesitant, I asked Sean if he would come with me to the great Mass at the Cathedral. As though he knew why I hesitated, he answered at once, "Of course we'll go, macushla. It's something I never miss."

We stood at the back of the church, a solid block of humanity around us, and I drew myself up and breathed deeply, restraining a grin of pure pleasure. There was something oddly exhilarating about the occasion: the icy wind outside, and within the Cathedral the warmth of thousands of bodies (I thought of the warm breath of the oxen in the stable), the mixture of incense, flowers, perspiration and hope in the air, the candles—so many of them that they seemed reflections in a series of mirrors—and the crude primitive perfection of the nativity tableau, all blended into a poem of joy, a sort of unconscious *Te Deum*.

In the final analysis, I have no doubt that it is the joyful atmosphere of this most pagan of Christian feasts that makes it the best-beloved. For the vast majority of those who celebrate it, I think the element of personal rejoicing overshadows the religious significance of the day. For me, as for so many who conform partly because it is easier, it was always a return to childhood, an escape into an untroubled past of irresponsibility and the conviction that the future brought only the desirable—presents, surprises, lights, music and the tangible evidence of being loved.

High Mass, with the familiar sung responses, the long-known and well-beloved *Gloria*, the hackneyed and infinitely dear *Adeste*, rolled on around me—the hypnotism of the organ, the heart-piercing sweetness of the little choirboys' trebles, and the deeper satisfying basses of the priests, all contributed to the euphoria.

Sean stood beside me, his face peaceful and bright, his eyes glued to the radiance of the high altar. His presence was good, but I felt the pleasure of being alone in my enjoyment that certain experiences bring—a sort of hugging to oneself of a happiness that needs no one, and that one guards almost jealously from even the tenderest participation.

As the huge bells rang out I thought that this was truly the essence of grace—the oneness—and I ruefully admitted to myself that, if religions sometimes failed, it was because the splendid stagecraft and pageantry could endear themselves only to the right mood, and must at other times repel the sobriety of conscientious reflection. Gladly I abandoned the fruitless musings, and let myself be borne off again into joyful acceptance of the easy moment.

There was a kind of acid pleasure in the sight of the communicants, wave upon wave of them, marching to the altar rails, the serious solemnity of their faces at variance with the anticipation they must be feeling—their hands folded, their eyes cast down, a brief *andante* in the series of *allegri-vivaci* that composed the Christmas Symphony. I did not feel I wanted to join them, but at the same time I had the slight atavistic pain that exclusion from a familiar mass movement may bring.

So enveloping was the atmosphere and the mood that we stayed on for the Benediction and left only when the current started to flow through the great doors.

A friend of mine, a convert to Catholicism, laughed one day when I said I had been a Catholic but "was nothing now."

"Once a Catholic, always a Catholic," she said. "It's something you'll never get out of your system, however hard you try." As she spoke—for this was quite recently— I remembered that remarkable Christmas and the delight of celebrating it in the traditional way. Perhaps one is more closely tied to the tenets of one's youth against which one is not free to rebel than to those which permit discrimination. . . .

The streets were no better lit than usual, but the frost and the fallen snow reflected the lights more clearly and the faces that bobbed past, over dark warm bundles, reflected the brilliance like moon-daisies. Perhaps, too, some inner glow contributed to the outer brightness. We walked home at a brisk pace, in a silence too companionable and too contented to be broken.

The fires lit, the food ready, we sat awaiting our friends. There were favourite discs on the radio, and the joss-sticks which Sean said "gave me away," were burning gently, releasing the notion of pleasure. On the pretext of powdering my nose, I had a small weep in the bathroom— there are peaks of happiness which hurt—and refreshed, I returned to find Daisy and the others pulling off gloves and scarves, still holding their Prayer Books but already in the mood for *Réveillon*.

Now the reason for the festival was forgotten. It became a sort of general thanksgiving, a hedonistic pleasure in the taking of pleasure, an extravagant joy in extravagance for its own sake. Sean and I drank champagne because we loved it and it meant something special to us. The others drank what they liked. We all ate enormously and talked incessantly and, as we grew sated, the talk became less merry and more exciting. In the Irish way it turned to the supernatural—the subject that only gets a good hearing by bright fires with the company of those close to one for protection—protection from belief as much as from fear.

Tadg (known as Tygheen) had hollow eyes and lantern jaws—the thin face of a visionary and a rebel as indeed he had been—and his voice was very quiet and intense. He was Daisy's brother—and utterly unlike her.

"I never knew me father," he began. "He died when I was a baby and I never thought about him much. Daisy went with me mother to the city, but 'twas the grandmother brought me up on the farm. Now I'm only telling ye this because Sean doubts that we can really talk to the dead. Now another thing is—what I'm telling ye happened when I was twelve, and had no imagination. Listen now.

"I had three uncles and they lived with us. It was very dark one evening—not late—about six—and I'd been to the seven-acre to fetch a milker back. It was quiet along the road, and not a great way to go."

He paused and smiled.

" 'Twas the grand stretch for bowls, that bit—a good steady slope. Many's the Sunday I'd be bowling there with the boys from school. . . . But never mind.

"I was walking along telling over me lesson for the next day when me youngest uncle comes along and walks with me. He was after asking me how I was doing at school, and what lessons I liked, and did I beat anyone yet at bowling, and what place did I take hurling. I was flattered, for Jerry was me father's twin and never took much interest in me—and I talked me head off.

"Every now and then, he'd run his hand over his face, as if he was wiping something like a cobweb off it—and I asked if something tickled. He laughed and said, 'No—ye're an observant little devil.' After a while he left me, and I thought he was going on down to the village to the pub.

"There was a kind of happy feeling in me bones, for there wasn't much time for talk or anything but work on the farm, and though I got on all right with the uncles, Jer was my favourite. Suddenly I was terrible glad I'd been first at school ever since I started.

"I put the cow away, and came into the kitchen. The three uncles were sitting round the fire, and me grandmother was knitting.

" 'Yerrah, ye got back quick, Uncle Jer!' I said. ' 'Tis only five minutes since I saw ye. I thought ye was off to the pub.'

"Jerry stared at me blankly. 'Is it mad ye are, boy? I haven't moved from here since five o'clock.'

"Bewildered, I passed my hand over my face, as if to brush away my puzzlement, and my grandmother sighed as she looked at me.

" 'That's yer father's old trick,' she said. 'Sure, when ye do that I think 'tis him standing there before me, God rest his soul.' "

There was a silence. Tygheen had told his tale and said no more to prove his point; there was nothing to argue about. Somehow, as he sat looking into the fire, there seemed nothing unlikely about the story, and we were all convinced that his experience was genuine. Sean looked up and took a breath, then closed his lips firmly.

Other yarns followed, including a couple of banshees, a three-legged horse and a determined attack by the little people on an English tyrant (*circa* 1600), but none carried the same conviction, and at last a yawn here and there signalled the end of the *Réveillon*.

17 : A Wake and
a Wilderness

The pattern had crept up on me quietly and gently, so that I had not noticed its balanced shapes, the automatic relation of each of its component parts to the others. The design in the apparently separate occurrence of pleasures and pains, births and deaths, had seemed to be but the ordinary material of life—woven on an Irish loom, of course, but just warp and woof. Now, it grew plain and distinct as the black threads were led into their appointed places in the colourful tapestry. A few had been put in earlier—Phelan's twins, Ida—but the new ones were to determine the final outlines of the picture.

With the heart-stirring, painful perfection of an equation moving towards solution, the x's and y's began to drop out of my Cork. Each tragedy half-anticipated, each grief almost waited-for materialized to take its place in the pattern.

Sheila Murphy died. . . . Her wake was a grim, terrifying and incredibly beautiful thing to see. The grief of her father manifested itself in the traditions of his people—an atavism too deep to be denied by modernity or taste.

"Keening there will be, and music to speed the departing soul gaily"—and dancing and tears for the comfort of those left behind—great platters of food to stay stomachs when hearts are emptied, and drink, strong drink to sharpen the sorrow to sweetness and then to flood it away in the good warmth of living.

As we drove up to the farm my headlights picked out the gate-piers, white and naked, and my heart lurched as I remembered Sheila's brilliant hair against the stone with the same powerful lamp throwing a halo around it.

I knew it then, I thought wonderingly. I knew beyond doubt and forgot the knowledge. This seemed suddenly unforgivable and yet, what could I have done to alter the inevitable?

The farm was eerie with lights everywhere, flowers in breath-taking profusion, faces and voices everywhere. The half-whispers of so many made a loud buzz, and the music wailed and laughed in turn at the strange party for death. My flesh crawled.

People walked about with glasses in their hands—poteen and stout and whisky—the mass movement focused on a circle around the coffin, open and surrounded by candles.

They had dressed Sheila in a bridesmaid's gown of pink satin, elaborate and unbecoming. Her red curls had been stiffly arranged in symmetrical corkscrews on either side of the white face and in her folded hands they had placed a bouquet of American Beauty roses. She looked incredibly alone in the crowd—and there was a touch of petulance in the set of the dead lips, as if she felt she was not getting enough attention at her own party. It was purely horrible.

Tom Murphy was sitting by the fire with the older men around him. His eyes had the glazed quality of somnambulism and he was drunk equally on sorrow and liquor, plunged into a silence which seemed unbreakable. I remembered his calm, contented pose in the arm-chair by the fire, and the shrewd watching eyes that had followed his daughter's movements around the kitchen in such love and admiration—and pity swept over me.

Kathleen looked older and smaller. The bite seemed to have gone out of her completely and her eyes were large and gentle and rather vacant. Her grief was twofold, for she bore as usual the burden of the brother with her own; and Annie, in the noisy childish grief of the healthy young, was less than no comfort to them.

Only the two old uncles were unchanged. If anything, they seemed a little more sprightly, as though they realized that age was not the greatest attraction to death, and they were still enjoying the hearth and the poteen whilst the child received the last respects of her elders.

The wake was growing wilder and noisier under the joint effects of drink and rising hysteria, and a small crawling fear came over me, so that when Sean, very white and drawn, came up to ask if I minded leaving early, I was overwhelmed with relief. Pressing Tom's and Kathleen's hands with the murmured, "Sorry for your trouble," of Irish condolence, we left, and I was trying to shrug off the discomfort of the evening when I heard Sean groan very faintly.

"Darling, what is it ever?" I asked in alarm.

"Nothing," he replied. "Only this damned indigestion —it serves me right for drinking all that foul poteen."

Some instinct made me switch on the roof-light and stop the car. He was ghastly, his face screwed up with the effort to conceal his pain, and his body huddled down in the seat.

"Sean," I said urgently, "Sean, where does it hurt most?"

He tried to grin, and said it was probably a grumbling appendix. In an attempt to reassure me he added that it often happened, and not to worry.

I drove him straight to Doctor Cavanagh's, ignoring his assurances that it would pass in a minute. The doctor confirmed that it was acute appendicitis.

"Into the Mercy with you, my boy," he said firmly, and came with us straight to the hospital. On the way, he told us that it was lucky Sean had chosen this time for an attack. Doctor Wylie was in Cork. He was one of Ireland's most famous surgeons and the author of a textbook on surgical principles which was a standard work of reference for the Irish medical profession.

"And what's more," he added, "he's had his hands blessed by the Pope himself."

"A passport to Heaven for his failures?" asked Sean, smiling wryly.

The doctor frowned disapprovingly. "Anyone would think you were worrying, Sean. A troublesome appendix shouldn't make you panic?"

"Not yet, Bill, not yet," he replied. "But I know what you sawbones are. 'Tis sending me to Heaven with a blessing ye'll be if I'm not watchful."

After the gruesome day, the joke made me shudder—and yielding to an impulse, I crossed myself in the dark.

When we got to the hospital, Sean was borne off by the doctor, and I was left in the cool white parlour for what seemed an eternity. I leafed through the parish magazine without knowing what I read. I walked up and down the polished parquet floor, adjusted a rose in a silver vase before a statue of some saint. There was a faint odour of beeswax and sanctity in the room which I cannot smell now without feeling sick.

At last a nun entered, in the white habit and apron of the nursing orders, and bidding me sit, she told me that Sean was to be operated on in the morning.

"In a little while we'll be giving him a sedative," she said, "but before that, would ye not like to ask him if he'd like to go to confession?"

"Oh, no!" I exclaimed before I could think of putting it more politely.

The nun looked at me very gravely. She had steel-rimmed spectacles and her gaze was the more piercing for them under the straight black brows. One part of my mind noticed that she had a slight beard.

"I'm after asking him myself," she said. "But he wouldn't answer. I'm thinking he'd be more responsive if you did."

"But why?" I protested. "Surely it's more important that he should rest now?"

"Any operation can be fatal," she pursued relentlessly, "even a mild appendix. I think you should ask him. There is a priest recovering from jaundice in the room next to his, and he will gladly hear his confession."

I swallowed the rising wave of nausea.

"Thank you, Sister, but I think these are personal matters in which I shouldn't interfere. Sean is quite capable of making his own decisions. At what time will the operation take place?"

"Half-past six."

"Thank you. I suppose I may not see him now?"

"It is better not," she answered coldly.

"Very well, then. Good night, Sister."

I walked out of the hospital into the back street where the single light, about fifty yards along, shone on a grimy tavern sign, and forgetting the car, the doctor who would presumably have to make his own way home, in fact everything but the word "fatal," I pushed the door open and sat down jerkily on the bench just inside it.

The publican gave me a compassionate look. He must have seen thousands crumble on their way from the grim building across the road.

"Whisky?"

"Paddy."

"Double?"

I nodded and he brought it to me where I sat. I must have stayed there for hours. . . . At length I realized there were Guards drinking around me, and it must be late.

I rose stiffly, paid, and stumbled slowly towards the car parked outside the dispensary.

"Fatal," said the door as it banged. "Fatal," said the engine as it started. The word enveloped me: from all directions it came at me, and fear was on me as never before.

Ridiculous, ridiculous . . . the simplest of operations . . . a scar the size of a pin . . . up and about within a couple of days . . . nothing to it.

"Fatal, Fatal, Fatal. . . ."

With the second sight that was becoming a cancer in me, I was sure—absolutely sure—that Sean would die and then I should have nothing.

I was at the hospital at six—in the parlour through which I am certain the souls pass on their way to Hell— and at seven a little novice with fresh cheeks and a squint brought me tea and biscuits. I don't remember whether I thanked her.

At eight I went out into the great entrance hall—empty and white and forbidding. There was utter silence: no one to ask, no one to attack.

I returned to the parlour.

When the clock said eight-thirty, the Sister I had spoken to the night before came in, smiled frostily, and told me the operation had been successfully performed.

In babbling relief I pressed her for details. Yes, of course he had had an anaesthetic. No, I could not see him until the evening. Yes, he was asleep now. I could come back at four.

I have no recollection of the hours between—at four I was standing in the doorway of a private room—speechless and terrified.

His bed was tilted so that his head was at least a foot lower than his feet. A nun sat beside the bed, passing her rosary through her fingers, watchful but serene.

He was awake and quite motionless. By some almost superhuman effort he dragged a smile for me to his lips—it could not quite reach his eyes. I tried to smile back and took his hand—hot, and limp and dry. The nun brought me a chair and I sat beside him wordlessly, trying desperately hard not to show my horror at his appearance. He looked terribly old and tired, and I forced myself to remember that the Sister had said "successfully."

This first visit was a silent one. There was too much pity and gratitude in me for words, and he was too exhausted and still numb from drugs. It was also a very brief visit—but my sense of relief, of a sentence commuted, was so overwhelming that on my way home to a much-needed night's rest I laughed, a little tremulously, at my panic of the day before.

In the morning, the fever had dropped and Sean was free from pain or even discomfort. Although the nurse and I insisted that he conserve his energies, he talked quite a lot.

A strange thing had happened—the secrecy, or perhaps I should say the reticence, with which he had surrounded his affairs, seemed to have vanished completely.

Perhaps in the intensity of his physical suffering, the sorrows and shames of an earlier period lost their importance. Or maybe he was at last aware that I loved him absolutely, and that no revelations could affect my feelings.

Whatever the reason, he seemed inclined to reminisce —in the manner of one who has had sudden occasion to take stock—and during the few hours each day I was allowed to be with him, I learned from him all the answers to the questions I had never asked.

He told me of his childhood—the idolized only son, the messiah of a family as old and tired as the Jews, waiting desperately for the vindication of hopes almost stilled. He spoke simply of his successes at school and the brilliance he had displayed as a student, as though he were talking about someone else.

"And then, of course, nothing would do for them but that I should go to Maynooth. They couldn't imagine my wanting anything else—and really, I didn't mind. It seemed a good idea, and I was keen to please them. They were already rather old, you see, and it seemed a small price to pay for their satisfaction."

He fell silent, and I waited, holding my breath.

"And then, darling, quite suddenly I realized that it wouldn't do."

Unconsciously I nodded in confirmation of Father Flaherty's story.

Sean smiled faintly. "Is it checking up on me ye've been?"

The tears I had kept in check so successfully for what seemed an eternity threatened to overflow—and he put his hand on mine. "I'm only teasing you, mascushla. Cork is a small place.

"Yes, I was telling you about my 'desertion.' I couldn't have believed the Church could have cared so much about seeing me slip out of the fisherman's net—and the more they fussed and argued, the more convinced I was. So I went to France, and then there was the war—and, oh! so many small things—and the rest you know."

"Sean, darling, forgive me, but why? What made you suddenly care enough to throw it all over, when you hadn't cared whether you took it on or not?"

"Don't you know? Haven't you found it out for yourself? You get a lot of time for thinking in a seminary. I thought of the passion that was bound to come—I knew something like this would happen—and I couldn't put myself in a position where I should have to wave it away, or betray myself to accept it. I didn't, as some people thought, 'leave the priesthood for love'—but because I knew infallibly that some time I would—and I knew it would be for a thoroughly human and not a divine emotion.

"You can see how, knowing this, I couldn't build up the superb edifice of treachery they wanted me to. I tried to explain to them—to my spiritual fathers, I mean—not my poor parents. I told them I wasn't luxuriating in youthful pipe-dreams, that I wasn't a budding lecher. They begged me to reflect—to consider—to abandon this worldliness and to try to sublimate this knowledge, or premonition, into the supreme passion of religious devotion.

"What I simply couldn't make them understand was that it would have meant a complete transformation of myself: I was no mystic—no, nor even a particularly devout young man. I couldn't do it, and I wouldn't.

"But you know, when I'd gone, and later at the Sorbonne and in other places where I was surrounded by women, I wondered very often whether I hadn't been a dreaming fool, and this doubt stayed with me for years— that and the regrets I had about my people. That's why I've always been a rather half-baked character until a funny foreign woman bought a pub in Daunt's Square. . . ."

His words made me intensely happy. It was a kind of crossing of the *t*'s and dotting of the *i*'s in a story of which I had only heard fragments—and the letters spelled what I wanted to hear.

His painting, his war years with the Underground movement, his achievements and his failures, he dismissed as the less interesting parts of a varied life, preferring to dwell on the innumerable curious and lovable people and places he had known, speaking tenderly of friendships, of well-known cities and seas, of the prodigal kindness lavished on him by the gods of distance and laughter.

They were slow, quiet, cheerful conversations—a preparation in convalescence for a fuller and more contented enjoyment of normal life.

And then I came in one morning, my arms full of flowers and some funny pub story on the tip of my tongue —and I stopped in the doorway. The blinds were darkly drawn and only the small reading-lamp was on. The nurse was alert, and no more of the indulgent cosiness emanated from her. She was working again, not benevolently surveying a recovery.

" 'Tis rather a thick night I'm after having," he grinned wearily. "Be kind to a man with a terrible head, will ye?" I only stayed a few minutes—partly because he looked so tired and was obviously making a great effort not to alarm me, and partly because I had to know what had happened to him. What could have brought about the raging fever in the middle of a satisfactory recovery?

I was given all the details, but all that registered were again only the operative words "relapse," "complications," "may pull through," "with God's help"—"tonight should be decisive."

Perhaps they felt some compassion for me—or perhaps

they thought my presence could do no harm now, or might even be needed suddenly—so they let me stay with him.

He was asleep when I returned to his room—the long tragic lines around his jaw deeper, and the pointed eyebrows more sardonic after pain. I saw the white hairs in his black untidy curls and they seemed unbearably pitiful in the midst of the deeper tragedy.

He stirred, woke and smiled at me.

"It looks as if we've been indulging in a bit of wishful thinking, macushla," he said quietly. "I'm afraid this is it. No"—as I opened my mouth to interrupt—"no—be a good girl and don't argue with me. If I'm wrong, I'll crawl abjectly—but if I'm right, don't let's waste any of the time that's left. Do this for me, darling, please?"

In silence I nodded, but out of my desperate refusal to believe him, came the futile words, "Sean—fight it, please—you *can*, I *know* you can!"

"I can't—and oh! my darling, forgive me—but I don't even want to."

And as I watched him with my heart in my eyes, he receded from me—frighteningly fast—growing distant with the unconscious aloofness of the unhurtable. Nothing could touch him—not even I. It came to me like a sword-thrust that this indifference included me. He extended his affection only through an exhausting kindness, as if he felt that, not having any more suffering to do, he had the final duty of not causing any. Somehow, this was the worst of all—and now I envied him the coming death.

Out of a dry throat, in a voice that was not mine, I said, "Sean, my love, you're not afraid?"

"No—I'm not. It's a long time since I thought that hell-fire awaited the likes of me. Don't you think, macushla, it would almost be more terrifying to face the prospect of life everlasting? The deadly knowledge of having to go on for ever, even in the most perfect bliss? Can ye not see me now, yawning over my harp, stretching my wings in sheer fatigue?"

"I'm not afraid either—I'm just desperately sad."

"I'm sad too, darling," he whispered. "I'm heartbroken that we have had so little time. I'm torn with misery when I think of you weeping for me, as I fear you will. But I'm so tired, my love—so utterly tired. . . ."

He dozed a little, while I held on to him, almost afraid to breathe in my attempt to stop time by stillness.

Suddenly he looked up—completely awake.

"Oh, darling—look after yourself. . . ." He turned his face away from me and lay very still. . . . He died while I cried my heart out on his hands, which I still held tightly—he did it with the calm dignity and gentleness which had first made me notice him and think in the same moment that "he was a man to love greatly."

18 ❧ Of Conscience
and Charity

It had been snowing heavily and the streets were dangerous with slush and ice. I drove back very cautiously late one afternoon from the Distillery where I had been on business. Because I was going slowly and was alert to the threat of the slippery road, I was a little more observant than usual at the time, and as I steered carefully down the mean back-street where the Donovans lived, I noticed that the lights from their two rooms seemed uncommonly bright —and then that there were two large black cars parked in the street just outside.

They were police cars, and around them stood several Guards, blowing on their cold fingers, and stamping their heavy boots like cart-horses impatient to move on. I braked as quickly as was safe, and questioned one of them.

"What's going on, Billy?"

"I don't know exactly, Mrs. O'—but someone's either been done in or done away wid himself, God save him!"

Brushing aside his refusal to admit any unauthorized person, "not even yerself, Mrs. O'," I rushed past him and up the dark, twisting and smelly stairs.

As I burst in, all I could see at first were the broad

backs and shoulders of Guards, standing and crouching around the centre of the room. Then I realized that there was a police photographer at work—his brilliant lamps trained on the middle of the room, too, but the harsh white reflections invading every sordid corner of the place. Then I saw a grey army blanket covering a body—patched black boots sticking out ludicrously at the end—and completely alone in the corner, Mrs. Donovan. She sat straight up on a kitchen chair, grey and motionless, her hands in her lap, staring at the men milling around her with the preoccupied look of one doing a sum in her head.

She had returned from a day's charring to find the children locked out, sitting at the bottom of the stairs crying with cold and fear. Alarmed, she had called a neighbour, afraid that Paddy had gone out and got drunk, and perhaps hurt himself or collapsed on getting home.

They burst open the door and found him hanging from the main beam, quite dead. On the table was an empty bottle of whisky and a note to his wife. It was affectionate and cheerful, stating simply that he felt she and the children would be better off on their own—and for himself he was tired of feeling guilty and unable to stop.

"Please, God," he ended, "there will be as guilty as me where I'm going—wherever He may put me. Yr. loving husband, Paddy."

I had nothing left in me with which to give comfort—plenty of pity, but it was the detached pity of the intellect, not the compassion that hurts as it wells up. I obtained permission to take the widow away with me, and drove her, still silent and dry-eyed, to Daisy's.

Molly still spent a good deal of her time there, and I found them together in the snug. A whispered couple of words to Molly, and they nodded to me that they would take over.

Wearily, I put off until the next day the grim duties of friendship—the conversations with the police, the guarantees for the undertakers, some attempt to help the family to survive. I simply did not care any more—and yet I felt the absolute obligation to look after them as though they were my own—as, insidiously, my Coal Quay people had become my own.

It was a bore, a nuisance, an intrusion into my private world of misery—it never occurred to me that it was no concern of mine. These were the only concerns I had left—unconsciously I clung to them in the complete emptiness of purpose or desire that my life had become.

I had nothing to go home for, and drove aimlessly around, half-thinking and half-dreaming, the forefront of my mind occupied with the necessity for physical caution.

Suddenly I realized that I had been making an unconscious pilgrimage to the places in Cork where Sean and I had been together, each of them associated with some moment of pleasure or profound contentment. It was at the north end of the Coal Quay that this was borne in on me, watching the dark water, the symmetrical stripes of the street-lamps' beams on the cobbles, the two white bollards like squat sentinels of the surrounding darkness. Again I felt the beating of pulses, the wild sweet excitement of the night after we had the picnic, and I strained my eyes to see Sean's shadow moving away into the back streets. I shook myself and drove along the route we had followed that day, out to the country and the waiting circle of magic rocks.

It was a moonless night, but there was no cloud, and the stars were clear and of the cold northern blueness. I left the car and walked slowly to the little amphitheatre, my boots crunching on the snow and ice.

The smooth rocks were only a pattern now—an extension of the whiteness in a series of dimples on the black sky.

I stood among them in the deep silence of the hours before the dawn. The utter emptiness of the place, and the absence of any feeling of life there were infinitely welcome: for the first time since Sean's death I felt completely in harmony with my surroundings.

I stood stock-still in the circle, my hands in my pockets, my breath smoking in the frozen air. The confusion of feelings and attempted thoughts began to fall into some sort of order, to overcome the panic born of emptiness.

The vacuum created by the loss of a contentment which I had somehow always recognized as ephemeral, I could accept—if not cheerfully, at least with the resignation to the inevitable that lingers in the blood of those born in the fatalistic East. It was not grief that I found intolerable—there seem to be no limits to the pain the heart can contain and continue its normal muscular functions—but almost beyond bearing was the sick revulsion, more, the revolt against the wickedness of avoidable disaster, of a deprivation that could be traced directly to a human responsible agency.

Bitterness flooded me with the conviction that this calamity need not have befallen me: another doctor perhaps would have saved the life that had been squandered, probably on the altar of another brilliant textbook. And I knew —Dear God, I knew—that all of them were accepting this fatalistically, with solemn nods: " 'Tis the will of God." Just as they accepted the ravenous inroads of unchecked disease, of tuberculosis as a familiar in their homes, of death and destruction hurtling along in the wake of carelessness, superstition, obstinacy and dirt. God had to be blamed for the fruit of their own omissions, for only thus could they feel exonerated—and if they were to feel no guilt, they could only accept disaster with humility as Heaven-sent.

It came to me then that I hated them—I loathed them, the Irish. I loathed their faults and their sins against them-

selves, their wilful blindnesses, their totems, their glorifica-
tion of the lies. I detested their poverty, their hypocrisy,
their mad scrambling to return to the womb of time, backwards, backwards, digging up the past glories and covering
the present filth and squalor with handfuls of pious dust.

Love had gone out of me: with the deep, intimate love
had gone love for everything—all that had been endearing
in the people was nothing; the laughter, the warmth, the
patience, the absurdities, the courage, the spiritual qualities,
the close links with the fairies and the gods; even the weakness and the unreliability that had charmed as they do in a
child—all these I forgot. In the scales of that moment they
weighed less than nothing against the immense disgust, the
angry contempt that stayed with me in the cold night.

I felt strong in my bitterness, strong and old and in-
vulnerable and, squaring my shoulders, I left the enchanted
place without a look or farewell moment of softness, and
drove back to the dingy streets where dawn, dirty grey and
unlovely, was breaking over the rubbish-bins and the last of
the night scavengers.

No need for sleep now, only work and thought and yet
more work. No desire, no sudden light hopes, no fears to
feel with every nerve and muscle. Only a few material decisions to be taken, a sensible move or two to be made on
the chequer-board, a practical establishment of a new *modus
vivendi*.

I went straight to Daisy's—it was still very early, but
they were up. Mrs. Donovan, under their ministrations, had
at last emerged from her shocked silence, and had wept
most of the night—a welcome relaxation of an unbearable
strain.

Now she had begun to think consecutively, and she
begged us to get hold of her usual confessor that he might
perform the last rites for her husband. Daisy promised to

176

go later in the morning, as soon as it was suitable to disturb the good Father.

Looking at the spent, heart-broken, exhausted woman, I was suddenly worried by another thought: Paddy had deliberately killed himself. It was a long time since I had ever considered the matter, but I felt certain that there were severe strictures in the Church on suicides. I wondered whether he would be allowed a Catholic burial. Could a sinner of this magnitude be laid alongside the just in sanctified ground?

I knew the desperate importance the people attached to funerals, wakes and all the other paraphernalia of mourning, and I feared that Mrs. Donovan had yet more pain in store for her.

Paddy's body lay in the police morgue—colder than death for the ice-bound weather—over a week. During this time, the possibility of foul play was finally eliminated, and his widow fought desperately for his grave.

Argument succeeded argument, and at times it seemed that only the importance of his proper interment was keeping her alive. She ate practically nothing, and never seemed to sleep—and neither, during that time, did her confessor, who was with her always.

Everything hinged on whether Paddy had been "of sound mind," for there was none to know whether he had repented *post factum*.

She, the widow, who had spent years of her marriage in fruitless attempts to guard him from alcohol, now based her pathetic case on the empty whisky bottle. I can hear her voice, cracked with tears and terror, repeating endlessly, "But sure, 'tis drunk he was—and him not knowing what he was doing!"

Gently, with infinite kindness and patience, the priest

177

explained to her over and over again the rulings of the Church on suicide and the reasons for them. Still she struggled—to prove or at least to convince, that Paddy was not responsible when he took his own life.

Finally, whether through some divinely inspired internal casuistry or (as I prefer to think) through sheer charity in the purest evangelical sense of the word, the priest buried Paddy, not with the funeral pomp dear to Cork, but with a quiet requiem and the blessing that saved the woman's sanity. I was deeply relieved, though saddened to see her taking comfort in the decision that her husband had died drunk and insane, but within the Church.

Events have shown me time and again that only disaster, sudden and gruesome, can stir people out of their comfortable lethargy. The quiet, inconspicuous, long-drawn-out agony of year-long penury and pain awakens few answering echoes of pity or help.

Mrs. Donovan's tragedy was sufficiently dramatic to arouse interest and compassion. The impulsive people of the county crossed themselves and then bestirred themselves on her behalf, so that in truth, as Paddy had prophesied in his farewell note, she was better off than she had ever been with him.

Work was found for her, and better accommodation; clothes and food poured in from many sources; and sympathy surrounded her. The final responsibility was lifted from my shoulders, and I was again free and alone.

19 : No Loose Ends

Calmly and methodically, I took stock of my situation: another period of my life had come to an end as clearly defined as if a neat black line had been drawn to mark it.

Ireland had received and accepted me, and given me all it had to give. As its guest, I had rejoiced in beauty and hospitality and been presented with a rare and wonderful gift. Now, the gift had been snatched away; the beauty stirred me no more; the ugliness to which I had turned my blind side was everywhere. I knew I had outstayed my welcome, and prepared to go.

The Brewery bought my pub readily. Deirdre's favourite auctioneer assumed responsibility for my household goods. Molly was presented with my share of the "loans" on condition that she continued to look after the lame dogs who benefited therefrom. I knew she would do this.

In the flat, which looked curiously square and box-like, stripped of curtains and trimmings, I packed books, candlesticks, odd pots and ash-trays: the curious collection of miscellania that those who are alone cling to in their travels, as though in some way they represented the nucleus of permanence, as though their presence in each new impersonal setting established a link between a past and a future that cannot mentally be reconciled.

Finally, there was nothing more to do. Every material thing had been dealt with, and there were no loose ends.

Had I announced a permanent departure to my friends, there would have been endless argument and persuasion which I couldn't face—therefore I made it appear that I intended to take a year's holiday abroad, visit relatives, and so forth.

Daisy and the others accepted this decision as quite reasonable. The change would do me good, they said knowingly, and when I returned, I'd certainly get a bigger and better pub. "Yerrah, the Brewery will be after offering ye one, now they know ye. . . ."

I felt a wry amusement at their conviction that I should come back—not unmixed with pleasure—for to them I was Irish by then, and an Irishman who goes "over" always intends, some time, to return.

So there were no protracted adieux, and no recriminations—just the odd handshake here and there, and the few farewell drinks with the old friends—as a *bon voyage* gesture, and not a sign of parting.

Tom Flynn came to the boat with me. We drove down in the Standard, which I was taking with me, and he talked cheerfully all the way to the docks.

"I envy you, sure," he said. "If I could, I'd spend a few months abroad every year. One gets to be a vegetable sitting in Cork. Think of it, this time tomorrow you'll be strolling down Piccadilly. Don't forget now, off Trafalgar Square— The Two Chairmen—I always have a few drinks there when I'm 'over.' "

Idly, I answered him as he chattered on, and casually I said then, "Why don't you go 'over' oftener then, Tom?"

"You know there's no one can manage the business when I'm away," he said reproachfully. "There's more than enough work for three of me here. . . ."

I could still laugh, even if it had to be secretly. Did he

really manage to convince himself that on those occasions several times a week when a serious hangover kept him from the office, his excellent staff didn't carry on quite comfortably? Was he really unaware that even in his presence, they did the bulk of the work? A publican knows more about people, sometimes, than they do about themselves.

There was no difficulty at the Customs, and none with the Immigration authorities. To go from neutral independent Ireland to England, or vice versa, must be the least complicated frontier crossing in the world, and as an old traveller, I knew the ropes anyway. My brogue, too, was so authentic by then that I was spared the indignity of being considered a tourist and therefore probably a smuggler of all sorts of goodies into the rationed land over the water.

The boarding arrangements are comfortably loose, and it is customary for friends to see passengers off on board, so that there was no chance for me to say what I ached to—"Good-bye, Tom, and God bless you!" Still the damned place clung—clung as it clings still today, and Tom came up the gangway with me, placid, pink-faced and slightly bloodshot as ever, the soul of kindness and of unconscious cruelty.

" 'The time has come, the Walrus said,' " he intoned, and deftly steering me past the cabin where my gear had been stowed, he seized my elbow and propelled me to the bar. He was still in his city clothes, and his bowler hat somehow looked odder than ever among the peaked caps, the scarves and the sailors' uniforms.

There was all the customary clangour of a ship about to sail—the delicious smell of linoleum, rubber, hot oil, brasso, seaweed, stew and a mysterious something that I have never identified but that all ships have, rose to my hungry nostrils. The excitement of boarding a ship is the only one that never suffers from one's emotional condition.

People threw bags and cases around, navvies shouted,

women wept, children screamed and laughed, and men lit pipes and behaved with unnatural calm and composure.

As a sort of basso accompaniment, the engines throbbed as steam was worked up, and a gentle vibration made each handrail quiver as one climbed the companionways; the very furniture seemed to breathe with one's body as one sat.

Tom smiled at me comfortably, and ordered the usual from the barman, to whom he appeared to be surprisingly well-known for one who travelled seldom.

Our conversation continued along accustomed lines—rather facetious and inconsequential—perhaps almost deliberately more frivolous than usual. Neither of us had ever mentioned, nor would ever mention, that moment of silent conversation at Crosshaven.

Suddenly the first whistle went, and the loudspeakers began to bellow the old "Passengers on board . . . visitors ashore" routine. I gathered up bag and gloves, prepared to make the final gestures.

"You know," said Tom, "it's Friday, after all, and there's not much I can be doing in the office—and nice weather for a trip too. Yerrah, I'll do the 'spin' with you!"

"But, Tom, you lunatic," I protested, "you haven't got a ticket, and you haven't told anyone you're going, and anyway, there probably isn't a cabin for you. How on earth can you stay on board? You haven't even got a toothbrush or your pyjamas, and anyway, I bet you didn't bring your passport."

"And who'd be asking a good Irishman who's doing the round trip for a passport?" he asked mockingly. "Sure the company will be delighted to have the extra fare, and it wouldn't be the first time I'd done the trip just for a pleasant way of spending the night! Sure, if 'tis the only way I'm likely to spend it with you, macushla, 'twould be worth it!"

He grinned so expansively, like a naughty schoolboy,

that even through my depression I couldn't help grinning too—it was so very typical of Tom and of Cork.

The ships that do the Cork-Fishguard run are equipped with stabilizers, which meant to me that instead of rolling and pitching gently as do other vessels, they roll over very slowly and then right themselves with an abruptness which is disconcerting. I took a couple of tablets as a precaution against the "stability" and suggested to Tom that we have a wash and brush-up and then dinner.

He laughed in my face. "If it's a wash ye want—then go and have it. And if you think you can get rid of me the same way as ye're throwing Ireland overboard—think again. Go and do what you want to, and I'll be waiting for you here —and don't be long, or I'll come and bash on your cabin door and make a scandal for ye!"

His playful toughness surprised me a little, but I obeyed meekly, mainly because I didn't care what I did. In a way, the nuisance value of Tom was something to take my mind off the more pressing realities, and in that capacity I welcomed it.

Washed, refreshed, and very touched in spite of my chilled insides by the huge bunch of hideous begonias from "yer friends at the pub," I returned to the bar.

Tom was in wonderful form—already a little drunk in a pleasant, convivial sort of way, his eyes popping more than ever, his face pinker, his collar just that fraction tighter that gave him the look of an apoplectic Pekingese.

Suddenly I was terribly grateful to him for his deliberate importunity—for blurring the transition so effectively —and I determined to be at least as pleasant as he was, if only to leave a good taste in the mouth.

He was ordering our usual poison—we shared a liking for Paddy whisky drunk straight in very small glasses— a sensible way to drink in those parts.

Our talk followed a rather Lewis Carroll pattern—

183

Tom was an authority on *Alice*, which I also loved—and I saw that he was making a great effort to give me as much pleasure out of the odd occasion as he could. At that moment I was very close to tears, for the warm Irish thing had suddenly appeared again, and I didn't want to feel any more affection, or any emotion at all. The indifference that had been my safeguard for the past weeks seemed the only protection I had against an antagonistic set of circumstances.

"For Christ's sake, Tom," I said, "be offensive and make me loathe you. Pretend I'm Moira. . . ."

His heavy lids lifted slightly at the gruesome bad taste of my remark. He smiled, and his smile was always ineffably charming.

"If I could pretend that, 'tis in your cabin we'd be now —and I won't say I haven't thought of it in the past once or twice. But you're not at your most attractive these days, macushla, and in any case you're a friend who's leaving me.

"Tell me," he went on, without pausing, "why did you tell no one you were going for good?"

So my elaborate pretence had not deceived him at any rate.

It took me a moment or two to answer him. I was ashamed of my outburst and didn't want to be beastly again.

"Listen, Tom—if you wanted to sneak out of a house without disturbing anyone, quickly and quietly, would you insist on rousing everyone and shaking hands with them before doing it?"

"I know what you mean, you fool, but why do you want to 'sneak out'? Can't you just walk out and slam the front door behind you?"

"Oh, Tom," I protested. "How could one do that to people like Daisy and Phelan? They'd be frightfully hurt. This way, they just think I've got Irish itchy feet, and they take it for granted that I'll be back."

"In other words, you care about hurting the feelings of people like Daisy and Phelan? If that matters, then they still matter to you."

"Of course they do, you ass, but only inasmuch as I wouldn't want to upset them; anyway, why should I?"

"If you'd really stopped caring about them, as you think you've stopped caring about anything, in Ireland at least, it wouldn't worry you whether they were hurt or not.

"I'm sorry, macushla, but you'll have to face it. Just now you hate Ireland and you loathe us—but it's a lovers' quarrel."

"Tom, you're idiotic. I just feel, as Agatha Christie would put it, that I want to 'get away from the scene of the crime.' "

"You feel," he went on as if I hadn't spoken, "that if you stay with us any longer you'll vomit or kill someone —you feel that we're unforgivable, and you feel, although you don't admit it, that if you didn't go now, you might succumb to the plague of Ireland—you might begin to push the undesirable away from you and wrap it in a cloak of destiny—you might become weak as we are, you might even accept the beastliness of humanity, as we accept it.

"You've become too Irish, and you feel too much with us, and your guilt weighs upon you because you feel this way and yet you still think. If Sean had lived, you would have welcomed this mental annihilation as the peak of your human happiness.

"Let's have a drink. . . ."

We sat in the warm rubber-scented saloon, and the ship rocked and returned swiftly to vertical—rocked again and again sprang back.

Tom talked better and better—and I wondered whether the suspended state of intoxication brought with it sharpened intuition, so that he was closely attuned to the taut-ness of nerves stretched almost beyond feeling-point.

Outside it was bitterly cold, and suddenly I visualized the immigrants on the open decks, frozen to the marrow, terrified as one must be even of the most promising future, whilst we sat cosily drinking—numbing all the hurts into blankness, deliberately denying the existence of suffering within ourselves, and so prevented from considering the possibility of it in other lives. That would have brought it too close.

Suddenly Tom said, "Do you know why we drink so much?"

Involuntarily flippant, I replied, "Do we?"

"Ah, don't be arch, you fool," he said. "It doesn't suit you.

"You know I'm irrevocably lost. You are, too. Not as far gone yet, but it's coming. And it's just, as all the psychologists will tell you, maladjustment. Everything is so much less trying when you're just slightly pie-eyed. And then, you see, between that and being really drunk, there's only a matter of a few greedy moments. We're both greedy—you and I—and you'll find your comfort there as I do—for it won't be anywhere else. I know. . . ."

Out of the callousness of personal suffering, I realized that Tom's purgatory was something I had not properly evaluated. Mine was temporary and definite and tolerable. His was vague, everlasting, and shifted like the sands in various moods. For the first time in what seemed an eternity I felt a little pain that was not purely selfish, and I asked him hesitantly, "Tom, is it because you must that you and Moira stay with each other, although anyone can see it doesn't work?"

"No," he replied, again with that disarming smile. "I stay, because I think she's still the most attractive woman

I've ever met—even though she's a bitch. When I want to smack her face is when I most want to make love to her. It's one of those perfect vicious circles: she's only unbearable because she's so utterly unhappy, and she's only unhappy because I'm not her dear little brother Reginald—and she can never marry dear Reggie—and that's why she stays with me." His hooded eyes clouded suddenly in momentary spite. "Sometimes," he added.

In the silence that followed, Tom stood up. "Can ye hear it?" he asked.

I listened for whatever I was supposed to hear, and then very faintly over the noise of conversation in the saloon and the throb of the engines, I heard distant and reedy sounds which resolved themselves into someone playing the gadget.

Stupidly, I looked around to see where it was coming from, and Tom, standing over me, laughed aloud.

"It's on the second-class deck," he said. "Is there enough Irish in ye left for Ceilidh?"

By then the rhythms were clearer, and unconsciously my foot was tapping already. Ah, Tom—you knew me very well! I jumped up at once, and we threaded our way aft and down the companion-way to the second-class quarters. As we went, the music grew louder and more compelling, and at last we came out onto the deck. I was faced with a scene so national that it seemed a dream.

Miles from the mainland, on the choppy sea, the pernicious Atlantic wind trying uselessly to quell the fire of it, was a typical cross-roads dance. With a fantastic backdrop of battered suitcases and humble household belongings roped together—it was quite unreal and somehow completely natural.

Formally Tom extended his arm. I took it, and then we were part of the whirling, hopping, singing and occasionally lurching crowd. Tom was a good dancer, and his national feeling had led him to devote a great deal of time to Ceilidh. He had the native sense of rhythm and was unself-conscious, so that it was a joy to follow the intricate pattern of the dance with him.

The deck was wide at this point—amidships and clear of obstructions, so that the "Waves of Tory" rose and fell in the long succession of twenty or thirty couples with the precision of an army exercise and the smoothness of a romantic ballet.

The dancers wore shabby dismal clothes: the women in coats too short and square-shouldered, skimpy skirts and down-at-heel shoes; the men in ancient sports jackets, shirts destined to bear long-gone collars, and heavy boots. Had they been in a queue, their very faces would have matched their attire; the atmosphere could only have been one of hardship and a blend of tenuous hope and utter despair. But they were not in a queue, and they were radiant; their faces alight, their ill-shod feet those of inspired performers, the familiar tunes a life-giving drug that transformed misery and cold into a merriment the more joyous as it was ephemeral, the more personal as it was shared.

We must have looked odd, Tom and I—he with his bowler and I in my good travelling-clothes and high heels. Yet with the good manners of the poor, no one stared at us or, indeed, took any notice of us, except to smile the welcome that embraced everyone.

We danced on and on, the cold warding off exhaustion, the rapid rhythms stirring the blood and keeping the laughter on blue lips.

Against a stanchion, sitting on a suitcase, an old army blanket around his shoulders, the gadget-player played on and on, too—his face that of a seer, his fingers resisting the numbness the jealous Irish Sea would wrap around them.

Only once or twice did he repeat a tune, and then only when asked, nay, wheedled, to return to a favourite. He was fat and sallow, middle-aged and ugly: as we whirled round near to him, I suddenly thought he looked like one of those mediums that fashionable women seek out when their comfortable lives grow too dull and unrewarding. His instrument was old and reedy, but each melody was a part of the man, so that it emerged as a living thing, unsubjected to the vagaries of wind and "gadgets" or consecutive thought.

The heart-stirring oneness with the other dancers grew stronger and sweeter, and the neat wrapping of cellophane around my refrigerated feelings began to dissolve. Suddenly I realized I was dancing like a woman possessed, and the tears were running down my face. Each step was accompanied by a sob, whether of gratitude or of grief, it didn't matter.

Tom beamed down at me. "That's more like it," he said. "That's the likes of Mrs. O' again! Yerrah, girl—it was a monument you were becoming!"

Finally, sheer exhaustion took its toll and one by one the couples moved to the edges of the crowd and took up their weary stations against bulkheads and rails until the dawn should announce the imminent end of the journey.

Like a tuning-fork, the gadget-player set the new note: he turned to the agonizing sentiment of the ballad; the age-old lament for the lost leprechauns; the eternal return to the Irish womb, longed for before even the completion of the birth.

"I'll Take You Home Again, Kathleen. . . ."

"Galway Bay. . . ."

"The Mountains of Mourne. . . ."

"Danny Boy. . . ."

They sang with him, and looking round, I found I was alone and Tom had gone. He returned soon with two stringbags (he had had some commando training, he once told me) full of whisky bottles, and these he passed around without a word.

Each took his swig and passed the bottle on. I was past worrying about germs and watched with delight. Like a litany, the "Slainthe's," "Yer health," "Geselle-guth's" followed each acceptance, and the smiles that went with them gave them the depth and beauty of a communion. I cannot describe the sweetness of the faces in their unexpected pleasure.

Unconsciously, I seized Tom's arm in gratitude and also, I think, in the love for the crowd there that had come back as abruptly as though there had never been the hatred. Some of the bitterness was still in me—but never again would it include the whole people which had incurred it and to which it was entirely owed.

There was too much to cherish in them—an identity compounded of every fault and virtue in the world made somehow homogeneous through a curious national quality. They could only, like some of those three-dimensional films, be looked at through spectacles of certain specific colours—and for a while I had lost those spectacles. Recovering them now, I recovered again the perspective which had left such a spinning blankness in its absence.

Dawn came, and with it the smudge of Wales on the paler grey of distance. We were still with the immigrants. Tom had made several supply trips to the first-class saloon, but returned each time immediately.

I looked around me and saw on every face the same weariness that was overwhelming me. Now the gaiety of the night, the bright illusion of unity and the sensuality of the music had gone. Only fatigue and fear were left, and the sense of exclusion that comes to all new expatriates.

As I watched, small groups began to move into the

rowded second-class saloon until at last only a handful were left. Then they, too, followed, and after a few moments I heard in answer to an inaudible *Introibo* the full-throated *Ad Deum qui laetificat*. I heaved a sigh of relief, for they had found warmth and comfort.

The fenders went out at last, and we bumped gently against the Fishguard quay. Hawsers went taut around bollards and the tug steamed away in the preoccupied manner of a bus conductress. Welsh porters began to stream on board.

Tom and I stood by the rail and watched in a sort of anaesthetized way the bustle of activity which had no answering echo in either of us. He was turning round with the ship, returning to his own treadmill between the intoxicated heights and the depths of disappointed sobriety. I was disembarking into a blank, unwelcoming future.

Finally, it became necessary to move—long after the others had left the ship.

"Good-bye, Tom. I'm truly grateful for this farewell party. God bless you!"

"No messages?"

"Only a general Slainthe—what else could there be?"

"I know, you fool. You won't come back—but you won't forget even when you want to. Yerrah, 'tis a fair enough exchange!"

And as I walked down the gang-plank to the shore, he waved the bowler hat, and shouted, "Top of the morning to ye, Mrs. O'!"